low Point cooking

over 60 recipes low in Points

Roz Denny

SIMON & SCHUSTER

A VIACOM COMPANY

First published in Great Britain by Simon & Schuster, 1999
A Viacom Company

Copyright © 1999, Weight Watchers International, Inc.

Simon & Schuster UK Ltd
Africa House
64-78 Kingsway
London WC2B 6SX

Weight Watchers and 1, 2, 3 Success 2000 are Trademarks of Weight Watchers International, Inc.
and used under its control by Weight Watchers (UK) Ltd.

Design: Moore Lowenhoff
Cover design: Jane Humphrey
Typesetting: Stylize Digital Artwork
Photography: Steve Lee
Styling: Maria Kelly
Food preparation: Sian Davies

Weight Watchers Publications Manager: Elizabeth Egan
Weight Watchers Publications Assistant: Celia Whiston

A CIP catalogue record is available from the British Library

ISBN: 0 68486 130 5

Printed in Hong Kong

Pictured on the front cover: *Low-Point Cottage Pie (page 33)*

Pictured on the title page: *Apple Batter Cake* and *Carrot, Date and Oaty Squares (page 70)*

Pictured on the back cover: *Pancakes with Strawberries and Ice Cream (page 78)*

Recipe notes:
Egg size is medium, unless otherwise stated.
Fruit and vegetables are medium-sized, unless otherwise stated.
It is important to use proper measuring spoons, not cutlery, for spoon measures.
1 tablespoon = 15 ml; 1 teaspoon = 5 ml.
Dried herbs can be substituted for fresh ones, but the flavour may not always
be as good. Halve the fresh herb quantity stated in the recipe.

V shows the recipe is suitable for vegetarians.

Contents

Introduction

Feeding your family while you are trying to count your Weight Watchers' Points is easy. There are lots of tasty meals and recipes you can all follow and enjoy without feeling you've got to stick to a miserable low-calorie diet. This book is a collection of much-loved family favourites made leaner and lower in fat, which is how most of us should be eating anyway. So, you should find lots of wholesome family food that will suit all kinds of meal-time situations.

There are quick snacks for one or two; dishes you can rustle up when you've just got in from work; ideas for when you want to cook something special when friends or family visit – and, perhaps most important of all, meals for you all to sit down and enjoy as a family group.

Nearly all the ingredients are easy to find at your local supermarket – but if you want to introduce a little variety to your meals you'll find certain store-cupboard ingredients like spices, herbs and white wine which will add exciting flavours for only a small extra outlay. The following items are a sample of what you may like to toss into your trolley next time you visit your local store:

Some Useful Storecupboard Ingredients
Dried herbs: oregano, basil, mint, dill and mixed herbs.
Spices: ground cinnamon, cumin, coriander, chilli powder and curry powder, and even saffron if you want to push the boat out.
Fragrant oils: extra-virgin olive oil and sesame oil add a wonderful flavour if used in very small amounts.

Wine: if you have any dry white or red wine left over, freeze two tablespoons at a time in ice cube trays to add extra flavour. Dry vermouth is a good substitute that keeps for ages without spoiling. *It is worth noting that when you cook with alcohol, you should make sure it all bubbles and cooks away as this burns off the Calories, leaving just the flavour.*

Fresh herbs: many supermarkets sell these in small packets. Fresh parsley is a good source of vitamin C. Green chilli, garlic and fresh root ginger can be bought in small quantities; they keep well if stored in the fridge.

Stock: you can buy tubs of fresh stock. Or try using vegetarian stock powder (the Marigold brand is excellent; it has a lovely natural flavour).

Snacks for One or Two

Here is a collection of speedy soups, dips, sandwiches and things on toast that you can rustle up in a matter of minutes. We've also given you details of how to make your own very-low-fat crispbreads – Melba toasts and croûtes using slightly stale bread – much nicer, and cheaper, than store-bought packets.

Ten-Minute Minestrone

Serves: 2

Preparation and cooking time:
20 minutes
Calories per serving: 135

Freezing: not recommended

Ⓥ

There's nothing like good home-made soup to fill you up and make you glow!

1 carrot, grated coarsely
1 celery stick, chopped finely
2 salad onions, chopped
500 ml (18 fl oz) vegetable stock (from a cube)
300 ml (½ pint) tomato juice
a good pinch of dried oregano or mixed herbs
40 g (1½ oz) quick-cook macaroni
125 g (4½ oz) frozen whole green beans, chopped
salt and freshly ground black pepper

1. Put the carrot, celery and onions into a saucepan with the stock, tomato juice and herbs. Bring to the boil, then simmer for 5 minutes.
2. Stir in the macaroni, beans and seasoning and continue simmering for another 5 minutes. Serve hot.

Cook's note:
You could also add 2 teaspoons of freshly grated parmesan cheese or 2 tablespoons of red kidney beans. Just add ½ Point per serving for the cheese and ½ Point per serving for the kidney beans.

Points per serving: 1
Total Points per recipe: 2

Fish Fingers with Cucumber Salad

Serves: 1

Preparation and cooking time:
15 minutes
Calories per serving: 180

Freezing: not recommended

Some speedy home-made cucumber salad makes fish fingers special.

¼ cucumber
1 salad onion, chopped
2 tablespoons very-low-fat fromage frais or low-fat plain Bio yogurt
a good pinch of dried mint
a good pinch of ground cumin
3 fish fingers
salt and freshly ground black pepper

1. Halve the cucumber lengthways and scoop out the seeds with a teaspoon. Chop the flesh into small dice.
2. Mix with the onion, fromage frais or yogurt, dried mint, cumin and seasoning.
3. Grill the fish fingers according to the packet instructions and then serve with the cucumber salad.

Points per serving: 3½
Total Points per recipe: 3½

Carrot and Leek Soup

Serves: 2

Preparation and cooking time:
25 minutes
Calories per serving: 100

Freezing: recommended

These two popular vegetables make a very tasty and healthy soup. If you don't have a food processor or blender, simply chop the vegetables finely and have a 'bitty' soup.

2 carrots, chopped finely
1 large leek, sliced thinly
2 teaspoons low-fat spread
grated zest and 1 teaspoon of
    juice of 1 small lemon
1/2 teaspoon ground coriander
500 ml (18 fl oz) vegetable
    stock
200 ml (7 fl oz) skimmed milk
salt and freshly ground black
    pepper

1. Put the carrots, leek and low-fat spread into a saucepan with 2 tablespoons of water. Heat until the contents begin to sizzle, then cover and turn down to a gentle heat and cook for 5 minutes.
2. Add the lemon zest and coriander and cook for another minute, then pour in the stock, milk and seasoning. Bring to the boil, then cover and simmer for 15 minutes until softened.
3. Strain the vegetables, reserving the liquor, and process until smooth. Mix back into the liquor and reheat, adding the teaspoon of lemon juice. Season if necessary and serve hot.

Points per serving: 1
Total Points per recipe: 1 1/2

Chinese Chicken and Sweetcorn Soup

Serves: 2

Preparation and cooking time:
15 minutes
Calories per serving: 250

Freezing: not recommended

This restaurant favourite is quite easily made at home.

2 teaspoons cornflour
500 ml (18 fl oz) chicken stock
200 g (7 oz) cooked and
    skinned chicken, chopped
1 salad onion, chopped finely
200 g (7 oz) canned sweetcorn,
    undrained
1 or 2 tablespoons light soy
    sauce
1 tablespoon finely chopped
    fresh parsley or coriander
salt and freshly ground black
    pepper

1. Blend the cornflour with 1 tablespoon of cold water and set aside. Put the chicken stock on to boil. Add the chopped chicken, onion, sweetcorn and can liquor, soy sauce (to taste) and seasoning.
2. Bring to the boil, then simmer, uncovered, for 5 minutes. Stir in the blended cornflour and cook for another minute or so.
3. Check the seasoning, add the chopped herbs and serve immediately.

Points per serving: 3
Total Points per recipe: 6

Grandma's Mushroom Soup

Serves: 2

Preparation and cooking time: 25 minutes
Calories per serving: 55; with fromage frais 60; with crème fraîche 70

Freezing: recommended

Rich mushroomy soup is always a welcome treat. Choose mature open-cup mushrooms for the best flavour.

2 teaspoons low-fat spread
1 small onion, chopped finely
1 fat garlic clove, crushed
250 g (9 oz) open-cup mushrooms, chopped finely
600 ml (1 pint) vegetable stock
1 tablespoon dark soy sauce
a pinch of dried mixed herbs
salt and freshly ground black pepper
1 tablespoon very-low-fat fromage frais or half-fat crème fraîche (optional), to serve

1. Heat the spread with 2 tablespoons of water in a large saucepan. Gently sauté the onion and garlic for about 5 minutes until softened.
2. Stir in the mushrooms, making sure they are well coated in the moisture. Cover and simmer gently for about 5 minutes, shaking the pan occasionally.
3. Pour in the stock, soy sauce, herbs and seasoning. Bring to the boil, then turn down to a simmer and cook for 10 minutes until softened.
4. Strain the mushrooms, reserving the stock. Process the mushrooms until smooth, adding the liquid back gradually. Reheat if necessary and check the seasoning. Stir in the fromage frais or half-fat crème fraîche to serve, if desired.

Points per serving: 1
Total Points per recipe: 1½

Sardine Pitta Sandwich

Serves: 2

Preparation and cooking time: 15 minutes
Calories per serving: 185; with tuna 135

Freezing: not recommended

Sardines are not only an excellent source of healthy omega-3 fatty acids (which are good for the heart), but also quite low in Calories if they are canned in tomato sauce. Here is a good light lunchbox idea.

1 medium pitta bread, preferably wholemeal
4 tablespoons shredded Iceberg or Little Gem lettuce
1 small carrot, grated coarsely
1 salad onion, chopped
1 tablespoon fresh lemon juice
a little chopped fresh parsley (optional)
125 g (4½ fl oz) canned sardines in tomato sauce or 100 g (3½ oz) canned tuna in brine, drained
salt and freshly ground black pepper

1. Cut the pitta in half widthways and slip your fingers inside to open it up carefully.
2. Mix the lettuce, carrot and onion with the lemon juice, seasoning and parsley, if using, to make a salad.
3. Roughly flake the sardines or tuna with a fork. Spoon some salad into the pitta halves, then divide the fish between the two. Top with the rest of the salad.
4. Press together lightly and serve.

Points per serving: with sardines 3; with tuna 2
Total Points per recipe: with sardines 6; with tuna 3½

Open Sandwiches

Serves: 2

Preparation and cooking time:
10 minutes
Calories per serving: with
prawns 130; with egg 135;
with Edam 140

Freezing: not recommended

Be sure to pile the sandwiches
high for an appetising effect
and eat them with a knife
and fork.

2 thin slices of rye or
  wholemeal bread
1 teaspoon low-fat spread
2 lettuce leaves
1 tomato, sliced very thinly
salt and freshly ground black
  pepper
Choose one of the following
  toppings:
• 60 g (2 oz) peeled prawns,
  thawed if frozen and patted
  dry, 1 teaspoon low-fat
  mayonnaise, a good pinch of
  paprika or mild chilli powder,
  a few slices of cucumber and
  a thin slice of lemon
• 1 chopped hard-boiled egg, 1
  teaspoon low-fat mayonnaise,
  a good pinch of mild curry
  powder, a few slices of
  cucumber and some snipped
  salad cress
• 2 thin slices of Edam cheese,
  2 teaspoons chutney and 1
  chopped salad onion

1. Spread the bread slices with the low-fat spread and lay a lettuce
leaf and tomato slice on top of each.
2. For the prawn or egg topping, mix the prawns or egg with the
low-fat mayonnaise, seasoning and spices. Divide between the
2 slices and garnish with the cucumber and lemon or cress.
Finally, grind some more black pepper over.
3. For the cheese topping, top each slice of bread with a cheese
slice, spread lightly with the chutney and finally scatter the
onion over.

Points per serving: with prawns 2; with egg 2; with Edam 3½
Total Points per recipe: with prawns 4; with egg 4½; with Edam 7

Tuna Pâté with Home-made Croûtes

Serves: 2

Preparation and cooking time:
15 minutes
Calories per serving: 265

Freezing: not recommended

Instead of buying a fish pâté
that may be high in fat, you
can make your own, which
will be much lower in Points
and will keep for 2–3 days.

100 g (3½ oz) canned tuna in
  brine, drained
150 g (5½ oz) low-fat plain
  yogurt or 150g (5½ oz) very-
  low-fat plain fromage frais
1 salad onion, chopped finely
1 teaspoon grated lemon zest
  (optional)
1 teaspoon Worcestershire
  sauce
6 × 1.25 cm (½ inch) slices of
  French bread
a little low-fat cooking spray,
  preferably olive oil and garlic
salt and freshly ground black
  pepper

1. Mash the tuna with a fork until it is finely flaked and then mix
in with the yogurt or fromage frais.
2. Beat in the salad onion, lemon zest and Worcestershire sauce,
adding seasoning to taste. Set aside in the fridge while you make
the croûtes.
3. Preheat the grill and lay the bread slices on the rack. Spray them
quickly, then toast the slices lightly on each side.
4. Remove and cool them. When crisp, spread on the pâté. Allow
3 thin slices of bread per person.

Cook's note:
This pâté is also good on rice cakes (three cakes are 1 Point) or with
Scandinavian crisp rolls (each roll is ½ Point). Try dipping some
bread-sticks (35 g sticks are 1½ Points each, 7 g sticks are ½ Point
each) into it too.

Points per serving: with fromage frais 2; with yogurt 2½
Total Points per recipe: with fromage frais 3½; with yogurt 4½

Mexican Chick-pea Dip with Melba Toast

Serves: 4

Preparation time: 15 minutes
+ 20 minutes cooking
Calories per serving: 190

Freezing: not recommended

Home-made Melba toast is much nicer than ready-made toast and the technique is really easy. Remember that one slice of bread makes two toasts.

400 g (14 oz) canned chick-peas, drained
1 teaspoon garlic purée
¼–1 teaspoon mild chilli powder, according to taste
¼–1 teaspoon ground cumin, according to taste
a good pinch of dried oregano
200 g (7 oz) very-low-fat plain fromage frais
4 thick slices of sandwich bread
salt and freshly ground black pepper

1. Preheat the oven to Gas Mark 2/150°C/300°F. Put the drained chick-peas into a food processor with the garlic purée, spices, oregano, fromage frais and seasoning.
2. Blend to a smooth paste, scraping down the sides once during this. Scoop into a small serving bowl and set aside.
3. Now, make the toast. Lightly toast the bread until golden brown. Remove, cut off the crusts, then slip your knife between the two toasted sides of each slice and split each slice in two.
4. Lay the slices cut-side up on a tray in the oven. Leave the bread in the oven for about 20 minutes until they curl up and turn golden brown. Remove and cool, then serve with the dip.

Cook's note:
Make up a batch and store them in an airtight box.

Points per serving: 3½
Total Points per recipe: 14

A Duo of Dips

Serves: 1

Preparation time: 10 minutes
+ 1 hour marinating
Calories per serving: for the tomato and pepper salsa 30; for the carrot and beetroot raita 1½

Freezing: not recommended

When you're feeling a bit peckish, it's good to have a dip or two in the fridge ready to snack on without worries about heaping on the Points or Calories.

For the tomato and pepper salsa:
1 large ripe beef tomato
½ small green pepper, cored and chopped finely
½ fleshy green chilli, de-seeded and chopped (optional)
1 fat fresh garlic clove or 1 teaspoon garlic purée
2 teaspoons fresh lime or lemon juice
½ teaspoon salt
For the carrot and beetroot raita:
1 small pre-cooked beetroot (preferably unpickled), grated coarsely
1 small carrot, grated coarsely
150 g (5½ oz) low-fat plain yogurt
a good pinch of dried mint
a good pinch of mild curry powder
½ teaspoon salt

1. Skin the tomato by dipping it into a bowl of boiling water for 1 minute, then slip off the skin. Remove the core and chop the flesh finely, including the seeds.
2. Mix with the pepper, chilli (if using), garlic, lime or lemon juice and salt. Set aside for at least an hour to allow the flavour to develop.
3. To make the raita, mix the grated beetroot with the carrot, yogurt, dried mint, curry powder and salt.
4. Spoon both dips into separate bowls. Prepare a selection of fresh vegetable sticks to enjoy with the dips.

Points per serving: for the tomato and pepper salsa 0; for the carrot and beetroot raita 1½

Sandwich Selection

Serves: 1

Preparation time: 10 minutes
Calories per serving: with
chicken 285; with banana 335;
with carrot 265

Freezing: not recommended

A sandwich can be a very
healthy snack as long as you
take care to limit the fat. If
you use very fresh bread you
could do without any spread
on the slices. For an
interesting texture, use sliced
wholemeal or multi-grain
bread. Juicy sliced tomatoes
and thinly sliced cucumbers
keep the fillings moist.

2 medium-thick slices of fresh
  bread, about 40 g (1½ oz)
  each
1 teaspoon low-fat spread
1 lettuce leaf
1 tomato, sliced thinly
salt and freshly ground black
  pepper
Choose one of the following
fillings:
• 40 g (1½ oz) cooked and
  skinned chicken, chopped
  finely, mixed with 1 teaspoon
  mango chutney and 1
  teaspoon low-fat plain yogurt
• 1 small ripe banana, mashed
  and mixed with 2 teaspoons
  peanut butter
• 1 small carrot and 1 small
  courgette, grated coarsely
  and mixed with 1 tablespoon
  reduced-fat hummous

1. Spread the bread slices thinly with the spread, taking it right
up to the crusts. Lay a lettuce leaf on one slice and top with
the tomato.
2. Spoon your chosen filling on top, spreading it evenly. Season
lightly with salt and pepper. Press the second slice of bread on
top and cut the sandwich into quarters.

Points per serving: with chicken 4½; with banana 7½; with
carrot 4½

Soy Mushrooms on Muffins

Serves: 1

Preparation and cooking time:
10 minutes
Calories per serving: 250

Freezing: not recommended

Mushrooms make a marvellous
light snack, full of flavour yet
low on Points. Look for the
darker, chestnut mushrooms –
they have a richer taste. You
could use a thick slice of a
multi-grain bread instead of
a muffin.

low-fat cooking spray
150 g (5½ oz) button
  mushrooms, sliced
1 salad onion, chopped
2 teaspoons soy sauce
a few drops of sesame seed oil
1 medium muffin, split in half
1 teaspoon low-fat spread
freshly ground black pepper

1. Heat a small non-stick frying-pan and spray it quickly with the
low-fat cooking spray. Add the sliced mushrooms and onion plus
1 tablespoon of water.
2. Heat the pan until it sizzles, then partially cover it and cook for
3–5 minutes until the mushrooms soften.
3. Add the soy sauce and a few drops of sesame oil. Meanwhile,
toast the muffin slices lightly until crisp, then spread them with
the low-fat spread.
4. Pile on the mushrooms, grind pepper on top and eat
immediately.

Points per serving: 3
Total Points per recipe: 3

Fast Light Meals

When you spend all day at work and look forward to arriving home to relax and refresh yourself, often the last thing you feel like doing is spending a long time in the kitchen, preparing a meal. Ready-prepared chilled or frozen meals may provide one option – but not only can they be quite pricey, many are also high in fat and Calories. Here are some reduced-calorie ideas that are also quite economical.

Quickie Kedgeree

Serves: 4

Preparation time: 10 minutes + 15 minutes cooking
Calories per serving: 345; with barbecue relish 350

Freezing: not recommended

Canned fish is very healthy. It is ideal for use in quick hot meals like this family favourite, kedgeree.

250 g (9 oz) easy-cook basmati or long-grain rice
3 salad onions, chopped
500 ml (18 fl oz) vegetable stock
210 g (7½ oz) canned red or pink salmon
½ teaspoon mild chilli powder or 1 tablespoon barbecue relish
2 eggs, hard-boiled, peeled and chopped
1 tablespoon chopped fresh parsley
salt and freshly ground black pepper

1. Put the rice, onions, stock and a little salt into a saucepan. Bring to the boil, stir once, then cover and simmer gently. Do not lift the lid. After 15 minutes remove the saucepan from the heat (still covered), then set it aside for 5 minutes for the rice to absorb the steam.
2. Meanwhile, drain the salmon, reserving the juice. Remove any skin with the back of a table knife, then flake the fish and bones (they are an excellent source of calcium).
3. Fork the chilli powder or relish into the rice along with the reserved can juice, then mix in the fish and egg. Check the seasoning, reheat well and serve piping hot, sprinkled with parsley.

Points per serving: 5½
Total Points per recipe: 21½

Spicy Bean Potato Jackets

Serves: 4

Preparation time: 5 minutes + 20 minutes cooking
Calories per serving: with crème fraîche 300; with fromage frais 290

Freezing: not recommended

It takes about 15 minutes to microwave jacket potatoes for four. Scoop out and mash the flesh with red chilli beans and a low-fat soft cheese.

4 baking potatoes, about 200 g (7 oz) each
425 g (15 oz) canned red kidney beans in chilli juice
2 salad onions, chopped
2 tablespoons half-fat crème fraîche or very-low-fat plain fromage frais
salt and freshly ground black pepper

1. Score the potatoes round the middle, then microwave on full power according to the power output of your oven (check the manufacturer's instructions). This may take up to 15 minutes as there are four potatoes. You may also have to turn the potatoes for even cooking.
2. When the flesh is soft, cut the potatoes in half and scoop out the flesh (or most of it). Mash it lightly with the kidney beans and the can liquor, then mix in the onions, crème fraîche or fromage frais and seasoning to taste.
3. Pile the mixture back into the potato shells, and return them to the microwave for a couple of minutes or so to reheat. Serve.

Points per serving: 3½
Total Points per recipe: with crème fraîche 14½; with fromage frais 14

Crusty Bread Pizzas

Serves: 4

Preparation time: 15 minutes
+ 12 minutes cooking
Calories per serving: 260

Freezing: not recommended

Take a crusty loaf and make
up a speedy pizza, choosing
toppings to suit.

1 French stick about 30 cm
  (12 inches) long
$1/2 \times 350$ g (12 oz) jar of tomato
  pasta sauce
100 g ($3^{1}/_{2}$ oz) half-fat
  mozzarella, sliced or chopped
2 teaspoons grated fresh
  parmesan
several pinches of dried oregano
  or mixed herbs
freshly ground black pepper
Choose 1 or 2 of these
toppings:
• 1 small green pepper, cored
  and sliced thinly
• 125 g ($4^{1}/_{2}$ oz) button
  mushrooms, sliced thinly
• 1 small red onion, sliced
  thinly
• 1 courgette, sliced thinly

1. Preheat the oven to Gas Mark 6/200°C/400°F. Split the bread
lengthways and place it crust-side down on a baking sheet.
2. Spread both halves with the pasta sauce, taking it right to the
edges. Then top with the mozzarella and chosen filling(s).
3. Scatter with the parmesan, oregano or mixed herbs and pepper,
then bake for 12 minutes until the cheese is bubbling and lightly
golden. Cut each slice in half and serve.

Points per serving: 5
Total Points per recipe: 20

French Eggs 'Sur le Plat'

Serves: 2

Preparation and cooking time:
10 minutes
Calories per serving: 100

Freezing: not recommended

Make a hot, light meal of eggs
and ham in a small non-stick
pan in under ten minutes,
then serve with wholemeal
toast and maybe some sliced
fresh tomato.

low-fat cooking spray (olive or
  garlic flavoured)
2 free-range eggs
2 thin slices lean ham, sliced
  into strips
salt and freshly ground black
  pepper

1. Heat a small non-stick frying-pan. When you can feel a good
heat rising, spray it lightly and evenly with low-fat cooking
spray. Immediately crack and add the eggs, then scatter the
ham strips over.
2. Season to taste and turn the heat down to medium. Cook until
the whites are set and the yolks still a little runny.
3. Loosen the edges with a palette knife, cut in half between the
yolks and slip on to two small warmed plates.

Points per serving: 2
Total Points per recipe: 4

Sloppy Joes (Creamy Mince on Toast)

Serves: 2

Preparation and cooking time:
20 minutes
Calories per serving: with
turkey 295; with beef 305

Freezing: not recommended

This is an odd name for
something absolutely
scrumptious. The great range
of lean, high-quality minces
that are available means you
can have a quick hearty meal
within 20 minutes, because
they are cooked so quickly.
Minced turkey is the lowest in
fat, but a high-quality minced
beef steak is a close second.
Serve on thick sliced
wholemeal toast.

low-fat cooking spray
200 g (7 oz) lean minced turkey
   or beef (freeze whatever is
   left over)
1 fat garlic clove, crushed
a good pinch of dried mixed
   herbs or 1/2 teaspoon mild
   curry powder
2 teaspoons plain flour
200 ml (7 fl oz) chicken or beef
   stock (made with a cube)
2 tablespoons frozen peas
2 thick slices wholemeal bread
1 tablespoon half-fat crème
   fraîche or very-low-fat plain
   fromage frais
salt and freshly ground black
   pepper

1. Heat a non-stick frying-pan and when hot, spray it quickly with
low-fat cooking spray. Add the mince with the garlic and herbs or
curry powder.
2. Stir well as the mince cooks so it becomes crumbly. Cook for
about 5 minutes. Sprinkle in the flour and cook for a minute, then
mix in the stock and seasoning. Bring to the boil, then simmer for
5 minutes, stirring occasionally. Add the peas and cook for another
5 minutes.
3. Meanwhile, toast the bread and place it on two warmed plates.
When the mince is nearing the end of the cooking time, stir in the
crème fraîche or fromage frais, check the seasoning and spoon on
the toast to serve.

Points per serving: with turkey 5; with beef 5½
Total Points per recipe: with turkey 10; with beef 11½

Spaghetti with Creamy Garlic Spinach

Serves: 4

Preparation and cooking time:
15 minutes
Calories per serving: 280

Freezing: not recommended

Low-fat garlic soft cheese and
a bag of baby spinach leaves
make a good quick, healthy
pasta sauce.

250 g (9 oz) spaghetti
200 g (7 oz) packet of baby
   spinach leaves
100 g (3½ oz) low-fat garlic and
   herb soft cheese
1 tablespoon light soy sauce
a little freshly grated nutmeg
salt and freshly ground black
   pepper

1. Boil the spaghetti according to the packet instructions. When
cooked, save about 100 ml (3½ fl oz) of the cooking water, then
drain the pasta and rinse it in cold running water. Drain it again.
2. Cook the spinach in a microwave oven or blanch it in a little
boiling water according to the packet instructions. Drain well and
chop roughly.
3. Return to the pan with the soft cheese, soy sauce and reserved
cooking water. Mix until smooth and creamy. Add nutmeg and
seasoning to taste, then toss in the pasta. Reheat until bubbling.
Serve in bowls.

Points per serving: 3½
Total Points per recipe: 14½

Carrotty Carbonara Pasta

Serves: 2

Preparation and cooking time:
20 minutes
Calories per serving: 340; with
poppy seeds 355

Freezing: not recommended

A nice vegetarian-style pasta
dish that's bound to please
all the family. Carbonara
is traditionally made with
bacon, but this dish uses
grated carrot. You could add
bacon flavour with a little
snipped, crisply grilled rasher.
Add the Points for the bacon.

125 g (4½ oz) pasta e.g.
  tagliatelle, penne or shells
1 carrot, grated coarsely
1 small red or yellow onion,
  chopped
1 egg yolk
2 tablespoons single cream
2 teaspoons grated fresh
  parmesan
1 teaspoon poppy seeds
  (optional but nice)
salt and freshly ground black
  pepper

1. Boil the pasta according to the packet instructions, adding the
carrot and onion for the last 5 minutes of cooking. Drain, saving
about 4 tablespoons of the cooking water.
2. Return the pasta to the pan with the reserved water. Beat the
egg yolk with the cream and cheese and toss into the pasta with
seasoning to taste.
3. Reheat the pasta very gently for a minute or so. Make sure it
does not get too hot or it will curdle the sauce.
4. Mix in the poppy seeds (if using) and serve in warmed bowls.

Points per serving: 5½
Total Points per recipe: 10½

Tomato Egg Foo Yung

Serves: 2

Preparation and cooking time:
20 minutes
Calories per serving: 195

Freezing: not recommended

This is the Chinese equivalent
of a Spanish omelette! Filling
and tasty too, it's ideal to
make if you have any leftover
cooked rice – otherwise you
will have to cook some.

100 g (3½ oz) cooked
  long-grain rice
3 eggs
2 teaspoons light soy sauce
1 large tomato
1 salad onion, chopped finely
low-fat cooking spray
a bag of prepared watercress
  sprigs
salt and freshly ground black
  pepper (optional)

1. If you have no ready-cooked rice then cook some – about
3 tablespoons of raw rice, according to the packet instructions.
Drain and reserve.
2. Beat the eggs with the soy sauce and a little black pepper. Quarter
the tomato and cut out the core, then chop it fairly finely and mix
it with the onion.
3. Spray a small non-stick frying-pan (about 20 cm/8 inches
diameter) with low-fat cooking spray. Add the rice, tomato and
onion. Stir for about 2 minutes until piping hot.
4. Lower the heat to medium then pour in the eggs, mixing them
in lightly with a fork. Season if desired and cook the eggs, gently
stirring occasionally, until lightly set. Tip out immediately on to
warmed plates and serve with sprigs of fresh watercress.

Points per serving: 3½
Total Points per recipe: 6½

Texan 'Bowl of Red'

Serves: 4

Preparation and cooking time:
25 minutes
Calories per serving: with beef
370; with turkey 360

Freezing: recommended

In the United States, Texans
call a bowl of spicy mince, red
kidney beans and rice a 'bowl
of red'. It makes a great fast,
light and filling meal.

200 g (7 oz) long-grain rice
low-fat cooking spray
250 g (9 oz) lean beef or turkey
  mince
1 onion, chopped
1 fat garlic clove, crushed, or
  1 teaspoon garlic purée
1 small red pepper, cored and
  chopped
200 g (7 oz) canned red kidney
  beans
200 g (7 oz) canned chopped
  tomatoes
2 tablespoons barbecue sauce
  or brown sauce
salt and ground black pepper

1. Boil the rice according to the packet instructions, then drain it
and set it aside.
2. Heat a large non-stick frying-pan. When hot, spray it lightly
with the low-fat cooking spray. Add the mince and stir well while
cooking so it becomes crumbly and lightly browned.
3. Stir in the onion, garlic and red pepper and cook for about 5
minutes until softened. Then add the beans (and the can liquor),
tomatoes and barbecue or brown sauce. Season and bring to the boil,
then simmer gently for about 10 minutes, stirring once or twice.
4. Mix in the rice and serve in warmed bowls.

Weight Watchers note:
For an extra 1/2 Point per serving you could top each bowl with a
tablespoon of half-fat grated Cheddar.

Points per serving: with beef 5; with turkey 4 1/2
Total Points per recipe: with beef 20 1/2; with turkey 17

Italian Lentil and Vegetable Soup

Serves: 4

Preparation and cooking time:
25 minutes
Calories per serving: 165

Freezing: recommended

Cans of lentils and mixed
vegetables can be turned
quickly into a tasty main-meal
soup. Serve it with chunks of
crusty warmed bread, adding
the extra Points as necessary.

1 onion, chopped finely
1 celery stick, chopped finely
1 fat garlic clove, crushed
2 teaspoons olive oil
425 g (15 oz) canned chopped
  tomatoes
1/4 teaspoon dried oregano or
  mixed herbs
500 ml (18 fl oz) vegetable or
  chicken stock (made with
  a cube)
1/2 × 425 g (15 oz) canned
  lentils, drained
60 g (2 1/2 oz) risotto rice
salt and freshly ground black
  pepper

1. Put the onion, celery and garlic into a large saucepan. Add the oil
and 3 tablespoons of water and mix well. Heat until the contents
start to sizzle, then cover and simmer gently for 5 minutes until
softened.
2. Add the tomatoes, herbs, stock, lentils, rice and seasoning.
Return to the boil. Simmer gently for 15 minutes until the rice
is cooked and the vegetables soft.
3. Serve in warmed soup bowls.

Weight Watchers note:
For an extra 1/2 Point per serving, you can add 1 teaspoon of freshly
grated parmesan cheese to each serving.

Points per serving: 2
Total Points per recipe: 8

Tofu, Pepper and Bean Sprout Stir-Fry

Serves: 4

Preparation and cooking time:
20 minutes
Calories per serving: 130

Freezing: not recommended

Tofu is very-low-fat soya
bean curd and an ideal main
protein food. For best results,
use a packet of smoked or
marinated tofu as it holds its
shape better. A good, tasty
dish for vegetarians and
omnivores alike.

200 g (7 oz) tofu, preferably
   smoked or marinated
2 teaspoons sunflower oil
1 red or yellow pepper, cored
   and sliced thinly
1 small red or yellow onion,
   sliced thinly
1 fat garlic clove, crushed
1–2 teaspoons ginger purée
   (optional)
200 g (7 oz) fresh bean sprouts
2 tablespoons light soy sauce
1/2 teaspoon sesame oil
1/4 small green cabbage, cored
   and shredded
salt and freshly ground black
   pepper

1. Cut the tofu into bite-size cubes. Heat the oil in a wok. When
hot, quickly and gently stir-fry the tofu until it is brown. Remove
and drain on kitchen paper.
2. Add 2 tablespoons of water to the wok then add the red or yellow
pepper, onion, garlic and ginger purée (if using). Stir-fry for about
3 minutes until softened.
3. Toss in the bean sprouts and cook for a minute or so until wilted.
Mix in the soy sauce, sesame oil and a little seasoning.
4. Sprinkle in the shredded cabbage and stir-fry until wilted, then
return the tofu and stir carefully. Reheat until piping hot and
serve immediately.

Points per serving: 1
Total Points per recipe: 41/2

Chinese Egg Noodle Hot-Pot

Serves: 2

Preparation and cooking time:
15 minutes
Calories per serving: 455

Freezing: not recommended

Instead of using a packet of
instant noodles as a snack,
make your own hot-pot – far
more wholesome and tasty.

200 g (7 oz) egg noodles
a few drops of sesame oil
   (about 1/4 teaspoon)
1 salad onion, chopped
100 g (31/2 oz) peeled prawns,
   preferably cold-water prawns,
   thawed if frozen
1 tablespoon soy sauce
100 ml (31/2 fl oz) chicken or
   vegetable stock, made with
   a cube
1 tablespoon chopped fresh
   parsley or coriander
   (optional)
salt and freshly ground black
   pepper

1. Cook the egg noodles according to the packet instructions,
then drain and toss them with the sesame oil.
2. Place in a non-stick wok with the salad onion, prawns, soy sauce,
stock and seasoning.
3. Reheat and simmer gently for 1–2 minutes until piping hot. Toss
in the parsley or coriander (if using) and serve in warmed bowls.

Points per serving: 6
Total Points per recipe: 111/2

Mackerel and Macaroni Casserole

Serves: 2

Preparation and cooking time:
20 minutes
Calories per serving: 495

Freezing: not recommended

Smoked mackerel is a rich
and nourishing fish, sold
ready-cooked. You can buy
it plain or coated in cracked
black peppercorns. Simply
peel off the skin and break
it into flakes – but do check
carefully for any stray bones.
This is nice with a green salad
or a bowl of lightly boiled
green beans.

150 g (5¹/₂ oz) quick-cook
    macaroni
1 small onion, chopped
100 g (3¹/₂ oz) fillet of smoked
    mackerel, skinned and flaked
1 tomato, chopped
3 tablespoons very-low-fat plain
    fromage frais
1 tablespoon chopped fresh
    parsley
2 teaspoons grated fresh
    parmesan
salt and freshly grated black
    pepper

1. Boil the macaroni with the onion according to the packet
instructions. Drain it and return it to the pan.
2. Mix in the flaked fish, tomato, fromage frais, parsley and
seasoning. Mix well, reheat gently until piping hot and tip into
an ovenproof shallow dish.
3. Sprinkle with the parmesan. Preheat the grill until hot, then grill
the dish until it is light golden brown. Serve immediately.

Points per serving: 8
Total Points per recipe: 16

Chicken Noodle Chow Mein

Serves: 4

Preparation and cooking time:
25 minutes
Calories per serving: 370

Freezing: not recommended

See how two breasts of
chicken can be made to feed
four in a light and lean way.
This is nice served topped
with a few pinches of toasted
sesame seeds. Remember to
add the extra Points.

250 g (9 oz) egg noodles
200 ml (7 fl oz) chicken stock
    (made with a cube)
2 tablespoons soy sauce
¹/₂ teaspoon sesame oil
2 teaspoons cornflour
2 small skinless, boneless
    chicken breasts (about
    100 g/3¹/₂ oz each), cut into
    small cubes
2 teaspoons sunflower oil
1 small onion, sliced thinly
1 carrot, grated coarsely
125 g (4¹/₂ oz) button
    mushrooms, sliced
70g (2³/₄ oz) garden peas

1. Cook the noodles according to the packet instructions, then
drain and reserve them.
2. Mix the stock with the soy sauce, sesame oil and cornflour until
blended. Set aside.
3. Toss the chicken with 1 teaspoon of the sunflower oil. Heat a
non-stick wok. When hot, toss in the coated chicken and stir-fry it
until lightly browned. Remove to a plate, add the other teaspoon of
oil and heat well.
4. Stir-fry the onion and carrot for 2 minutes, then mix in the
mushrooms, peas and blended sauce.
5. Bring to the boil, stirring until the sauce is glossy and slightly
thickened. Return the chicken to the wok and simmer for 3–5
minutes until the chicken is firm and cooked.
6. Now mix in the noodles and heat until piping hot. Serve
immediately in warmed bowls.

Points per serving: 5¹/₂
Total Points per recipe: 22

Sit-Down Meals

Mealtimes are often the best time for all the family to sit down together. There's something special about everyone talking about their day while enjoying a good feed! Such meals needn't be time-consuming to cook so most of the recipes here can be prepared in a very short time.

Low-Point Cottage Pie

Serves: 4

Preparation time: 15 minutes
+ 25 minutes cooking
Calories per serving: 340

Freezing: recommended

To make the mash really tasty, mix in a little coarse-grained mustard.

600 g (1 lb 5 oz) floury
    potatoes, peeled thinly
2–3 tablespoons skimmed milk
2 teaspoons coarse-grained
    mustard (optional)
low-fat cooking spray

250 g (9 oz) very lean minced
    beef
1 large onion, chopped
1 carrot, grated coarsely
1 tablespoon plain flour
4 tablespoons red lentils
400 ml (14 fl oz) beef stock
a good pinch of dried mixed
    herbs
1 teaspoon Worcestershire
    sauce (optional)
1 tablespoon dried
    breadcrumbs
salt and freshly ground black
    pepper

1. Cut the potatoes into chunks and boil them in lightly salted water for 12–15 minutes until tender. Drain, mash and mix in the milk, seasoning and mustard, if using. Aim for a soft mash that is not too runny.
2. Heat a non-stick frying-pan. Spray it lightly with low-fat cooking spray and immediately add the mince, stirring to break it up as it browns. Cook it for about 5 minutes until it is crumbly.
3. Add the onion and carrot plus a little water to moisten the mixture if necessary. Some minces give off juices as they cook. Continue cooking for about 5 minutes.
4. Stir in the flour, then the lentils. Add the stock, herbs and Worcestershire sauce, if using. Bring to the boil, season well and simmer, uncovered, for about 12 minutes until the lentils are soft.
5. Transfer to an ovenproof dish, then spoon the soft mash over the top. Level it with the back of a fork and sprinkle the breadcrumbs over.
6. Preheat the grill. When it is hot, brown the pie top until it is golden and slightly crisp. Serve immediately.

Points per serving: 5
Total Points per recipe: 19½

Turkey and Leek Tagliatelle

Serves: 4

Preparation time: 15 minutes
+ 20 minutes cooking
Calories per serving: 350

Freezing: recommended

Turkey is a great lean and light meat, sometimes as low as 3% fat. You can buy it in a variety of cuts – one of the most versatile is breast steak. Try it in a creamy mushroom sauce with pasta. This dish is good with cherry tomatoes.

250 g (9 oz) dried tagliatelle
    pasta
1 tablespoon olive oil
200 g (7 oz) turkey breast
    steaks, diced in 1 cm (½ inch)
    chunks
1 large leek, sliced
125 g (4½ oz) button
    mushrooms
1 tablespoon dry sherry or
    vermouth (optional)
a good pinch of dried tarragon
a good pinch of dried thyme
300 ml (½ pint) stock
3 tablespoons half-fat crème
    fraîche
salt and freshly ground black
    pepper

1. Boil the pasta according to the packet instructions, then drain it, rinse in cold water and drain well again.
2. Meanwhile, heat the oil in a large shallow pan and stir-fry the turkey meat for 2–3 minutes until lightly browned. Remove with a slotted spoon.
3. Reheat the pan, adding 2 tablespoons of water, and stir-fry the leek and mushrooms for 3 minutes. Then add the sherry or vermouth, if using, and cook for about 5 minutes.
4. Add the herbs, then the stock. Reheat to boiling. Turn down to a gentle simmer and cook for 15 minutes, then uncover the pan, season to taste and mix in the crème fraîche and pasta.
5. Stir well and reheat until piping hot, then serve.

Points per serving: 5
Total Points per recipe: 20

Quick and Easy Paella

Serves: 4

Preparation time: 15 minutes
+ 25 minutes cooking
Calories per serving: 470

Freezing: not recommended

Creamy and tasty, paella is a perfect family meal – it takes a short time to put together, cooks without much attention and needs little further accompaniment than a crisp salad or some steaming green beans. Saffron is the classic paella spice and gives an authentic taste, but you may omit it if you wish.

a pinch of saffron strands
  (optional)
1 tablespoon olive oil
4 medium skinned and boned
  chicken thighs, each cut
  in half
1 large onion, chopped
1 fat garlic clove, chopped
1 green pepper, chopped
250 g (9 oz) risotto rice
2–3 teaspoons mild sweet
  paprika
25 g (1 oz) canned chopped
  tomatoes
600 ml (1 pint) chicken stock
200 g (7 oz) peeled prawns
salt and freshly ground black
  pepper

1. Steep the saffron strands, if using, in 2 tablespoons of boiling water and set them aside.
2. Using a large, shallow frying-pan, heat the oil and quickly brown the chicken for 3–5 minutes. Remove with a slotted spoon.
3. Add 2–3 tablespoons of water to the pan and gently sauté the onion, garlic and pepper until softened, for about 5 minutes.
4. Stir in the rice, paprika, tomatoes, saffron water with strands and stock. Return the chicken to the pan. Season well, bring to the boil, then cover and simmer for 15–18 minutes without lifting the lid.
5. Uncover the pan, stir in the prawns and cook for another 5 minutes or so. Check the seasoning and serve.

Points per serving: 6
Total Points per recipe: 25

Teriyaki Chicken in the Oven

Serves: 4

Preparation time: 5 minutes +
30 minutes cooking +
marinating
Calories per serving: 290

Freezing: recommended

**Teriyaki is a Japanese sweet
soy marinade that is excellent
with chicken, beef, pork or
lamb. You can sometimes buy
it ready-made, but it is easy
to make it yourself. It is
especially good with meaty
chicken thighs. Boiled
basmati rice and mange-tout
peas or green beans go well
with this.**

8 medium skinless, boneless
   chicken thighs
For the marinade:
2 tablespoons dark soy sauce
1 tablespoon mirin (Japanese
   cooking wine) or medium
   dry sherry
1/2 teaspoon ground coriander
1/2 teaspoon garlic powder
1/2 teaspoon sesame oil

1. Trim any excess fat from the thighs and place them in a food bag.
2. Mix the marinade ingredients together and pour in the bag. Mix
together well and leave in the fridge for 1/2 to 1 hour.
3. Preheat the oven to Gas Mark 4/180°C/350°F. Tip the chicken
thighs and marinade into a shallow ovenproof dish. Cover loosely
with foil to allow a little steam to escape.
4. Bake for 30 minutes, basting once, until the meat is very tender.
Serve with the cooking juices poured over.

Points per serving: 5
Total Points per recipe: 20 1/2

Lemon and Soy Trout

Serves: 4

Preparation time: 5 minutes +
1/2 hour marinating + 15
minutes cooking
Calories per serving: with
trout 155; with salmon 215

Freezing: not recommended

**Fish is delicious grilled with
an Oriental-style sauce,
especially if it is an oily or
rich fish like trout or salmon.
Good with baby new potatoes
and fresh leaf spinach,
microwaved 'in the bag'.**

4 whole and gutted fresh trout,
   about 200 g (7 oz) each (or
   115 g/4 oz salmon fillets)
2 tablespoons soy sauce
1 tablespoon lemon juice
2 teaspoons clear honey
grated zest of 1/2 lemon
a little chopped fresh parsley
freshly ground black pepper

1. Wash the whole trout well under cold running water, making
sure you remove any dark blood inside the body cavity. Pat it dry
and put it in a food bag.
2. Mix the soy sauce, lemon juice, honey and lemon zest until
emulsified, then pour on to the fish and rub it in well. Marinate
in the fridge for 1/2 hour.
3. Preheat the grill, then place the fish on the rack. Cook for about
7 minutes on each side under medium heat, brushing any left
over marinade over the fish. Turn the fish carefully to try to avoid
breaking the skin. Season with freshly ground black pepper and
serve garnished with the parsley.

Points per serving: 3
Total Points per recipe: 13

Fish Balls with Creamy Tomato Pasta

Serves: 4

Preparation time: 15 minutes
+ 20 minutes cooking
Calories per serving: 365

Freezing: recommended

Fish balls are really simple to
make, as long as you have a
food processor. You will not
need to add an egg and there
is no need to pre-fry.

400 g (14 oz) skinless cod,
    haddock or coley fillet
1 large onion, chopped
1 teaspoon salt
1 tablespoon chopped fresh
    parsley (optional)
200 g (7 oz) pasta shapes
1 small red or yellow pepper,
    cored and chopped
1 tablespoon olive oil
500 ml (18 fl oz) passata or
    sugocasa (sieved tomatoes)
a small pinch of dried basil
2 tablespoons half-fat crème
    fraîche
freshly ground black pepper

1. Put the fish, half the onion, 1 teaspoon of salt and some ground
black pepper into a food processor and whizz until smooth, scraping
down the sides of the container. Mix the parsley in by hand, if using.
2. Now shape the mixture into balls. It's easy! Divide and roll into
8–12 balls, depending on how large you want them, and set them
aside. If the mixture sticks, dip your hands in cold water.
3. Boil the pasta shapes according to the packet instructions.
4. Put the remaining onion, the pepper and the oil into a saucepan
and heat until it starts to sizzle. Stir well, cover and turn down to
a gentle heat. Cook for 5 minutes until softened.
5. Stir in the sieved tomatoes and add the basil. Cook the fish balls
in the sauce for about 15 minutes or until they feel firm when just
pressed. Gently mix in the crème fraîche and the pasta shapes
and serve.

Points per serving: 4½
Total Points per recipe: with haddock 18; with cod or coley
fillet 18½

Crispy Cod with Lemon and Parsley Crust

Serves: 4

Preparation time: 15 minutes
+ 25 minutes cooking
Calories per serving: 140

Freezing: recommended

Use a whole fillet of cod for
this and use fillets with the
skin on for easier handling.
Adjust the Points as necessary.

1 large cod fillet (skin on) –
    about 350–400 g (12–14 oz)
    weight
low-fat cooking spray
3 medium slices white bread,
    crusts removed
grated zest and juice of 1 lemon
1 fat garlic clove, crushed
½ mug fresh parsley sprigs,
    chopped
salt and freshly ground black
    pepper

1. Preheat the oven to Gas Mark 4/180°C/350°F. Check the fish for
any stray bones by running your fingertips along the flesh. Pull out
any bones you feel with tweezers or your fingers.
2. Lightly spray a shallow ovenproof dish with low-fat cooking
spray. Lay the fish in it, skin-side down. Season it lightly.
3. Whizz the bread through a food processor to make crumbs,
then mix these with the lemon zest, garlic, chopped parsley and
seasoning. Mix in the lemon juice so the crumbs are moist, then
spoon them over the fish, pressing them down lightly with the
back of a fork.
4. Bake for about 25 minutes or until the fish feels firm and flakes
when you test it with a fork.

Points per serving: 2
Total Points per recipe: 7½

Plaice Flipovers

Serves: 4

Preparation time: 15 minutes
+ 20 minutes cooking
Calories per serving: 160

Freezing: recommended

Buy light-skinned fillets of plaice or sole, fold them over a light stuffing, then bake them. Nice with creamy mashed potatoes.

low-fat cooking spray
4 fillets of plaice or sole, preferably skinned – about 100 g (3½)
125 g (4½ oz) button mushrooms, chopped
1 small onion, chopped
2 teaspoons olive or sunflower oil
a pinch of dried thyme
2 medium slices brown bread, crusts removed
salt and freshly ground black pepper
wedges of fresh lemon, to serve

1. Preheat the oven to Gas Mark 4/180°C/350°F. Spray a shallow ovenproof dish with low-fat cooking spray, and lightly season the fish on the flesh side.
2. Put the mushrooms and onion in a small pan with the oil and a tablespoon of water. Heat until it starts to sizzle, then add the thyme and seasoning. Cover and cook gently for 5 minutes or more until softened.
3. Meanwhile, whizz the bread through a food processor to make crumbs. Mix the crumbs into the onion and mushrooms and season again.
4. Divide between the 4 fish fillets and fold them over to cover the stuffing, skin-side up. Place them in the ovenproof dish and bake for 20–25 minutes or until the flesh is cooked and feels just firm. Take care not to overcook. Serve with wedges of lemon.

Points per serving: 2
Total Points per recipe: 8

Pot-Roast Dinner

Serves: 4

Preparation time: 15 minutes
+ 2–2½ hours cooking
Calories per serving: with silverside 330; with rump joint 315

Freezing: recommended

Many supermarkets sell neat, lean, slow-roasting joints of beef that make good all-in-one pot roasts when cooked on a bed of vegetables.

low-fat cooking spray
1 very lean silverside or top rump joint, about 600 g (1 lb 5 oz) weight
1 onion, sliced thinly (ideally a red onion)
1 large celery stick, sliced
2 carrots, quartered lengthways
2 parsnips, quartered lengthways
1 green pepper, cored and quartered
2 baking potatoes, about 150 g (5 oz) each, sliced thickly
a good pinch of dried mixed herbs
300 ml (½ pint) beef stock (made with a cube)
a few dashes of Worcestershire sauce or mushroom ketchup (optional)
salt and freshly ground black pepper

1. Heat a non-stick frying-pan and when hot, spray it lightly with low-fat cooking spray. Add the meat and brown it all over by rolling it around. Remove.
2. Preheat the oven to Gas Mark 3/170°C/325°F. Put the vegetables in the pan, spray lightly, then cook on medium heat for about 3–5 minutes to seal and lightly brown them. (You may have to do this in batches.) Remove the pan from the heat.
3. Spoon the vegetables down the centre of a small roasting dish. Season well, sprinkle with herbs and pour in the stock. Add the sauce, if using.
4. Sit the meat on the vegetables and cover the whole pan with foil. Bake for 2–2½ hours or until the meat is meltingly tender and the vegetables soft.
5. Carve the meat into 4 slices and serve it with the vegetables and juices.

Points per serving: with silverside 4½; with rump 6
Total Points per recipe: with silverside 18; with rump 23½

Cauliflower and Broccoli Cheese Bake

Serves: 4

Preparation time: 15 minutes + 20 minutes cooking
Calories per serving: 200

Freezing: recommended

A favourite family supper – white and green florets covered in a creamy cheese sauce.

2 heads of broccoli
1 medium-size cauliflower
1 large leek, sliced thickly
300 ml (1/2 pint) skimmed milk
2 tablespoons cornflour or sauce flour
a good pinch of dried thyme or sage
100 g (3 1/2 oz) reduced-fat mature Cheddar, grated
2 tablespoons dried breadcrumbs
6–8 cherry tomatoes, halved
salt and freshly ground black pepper

1. Break the broccoli and cauliflower into small florets. Don't throw out too much of the stalks. They can be sliced and used. Place in a saucepan with the leek and pour over boiling water to just cover. Season lightly with salt, then bring to the boil.
2. Cover and simmer for about 5 minutes until the florets are just tender but not soft.
3. Strain off about 100 ml (3 1/2 fl oz) of the water and reserve it. Drain the rest. Leave the vegetables in the colander while you make the sauce.
4. Pour the strained water and milk into the same saucepan and whisk in the cornflour or flour. Bring the mixture slowly to the boil, stirring frequently until the sauce thickens and becomes glossy. Season and add the herbs. Simmer for 2 minutes.
5. Remove from the heat and stir in the cheese. Tip the vegetables into a heatproof dish and preheat the grill until hot.
6. Pour the sauce over the vegetables, scatter the crumbs over and dot with the cherry tomatoes. Turn the grill to medium and brown the top of the vegetables lightly.

Points per serving: 3
Total Points per recipe: 11

Cook's note:
To make your own dried breadcrumbs, use the crusts from 2-day-old bread which has dried out slightly. Set the oven temperature to low, and lay the slices on the oven shelf. Leave for two hours or until the slices become brittle and crisp. Remove and cool. Crush roughly with your hands and then pass them through a food processor or blender to make into crumbs. To make perfect crumbs, shake them through a sieve.

Irish Stew

Serves: 4

Preparation time: 20 minutes + 45–60 minutes cooking
Calories per serving: 460

Freezing: recommended

The perfect dish for a wintry night – sweet tender lamb cutlets simmered in broth with root vegetables!

400 g (14 oz) lean cubed lamb, trimmed of all fat
1 onion, peeled but with root end still attached
4 whole cloves
2 carrots, quartered
2 potatoes, about 150 g (5 oz) each
2 celery sticks, sliced thickly
2 leeks, cut in thick chunks
600 ml (1 pint) vegetable or lamb stock (made with a cube) or water
1 large bay leaf
salt and freshly ground black pepper

1. Trim as much fat as possible from the cutlets. Heat a non-stick frying-pan without any fat. When hot, dry-fry the cutlets quickly to brown them on both sides. Remove.
2. Cut the onion into quarters, preserving the core at one end so that the quarters remain intact. Stick a clove into each quarter.
3. Place a large heavy-based saucepan on the stove. Add the cutlets and all the vegetables (including the onion). Pour in the stock or water, add the bay leaf and season well.
4. Bring slowly to the boil, then cover and turn down to a simmer. Cook for 45–60 minutes until the meat is tender and vegetables soft. Serve like a stew soup and eat with a spoon and fork.

Points per serving: 4 1/2
Total Points per recipe: 18 1/2

Lean and Light Lasagne

Serves: 4

Preparation time: 40 minutes + 25 minutes cooking in the oven or 10 minutes under the grill

Calories per serving: 310

Freezing: recommended

Popular with youngsters and grown-ups alike.

6 lasagne sheets
2 teaspoons olive or sunflower oil
400 g (14 oz) turkey mince
1 fat garlic clove, crushed
1 onion, chopped
1 carrot, chopped finely
1 celery stick, chopped finely
425 g (15 oz) canned chopped tomatoes
1 tablespoon tomato purée
1/4 teaspoon dried basil or oregano
salt and freshly ground black pepper

For the sauce:
300 ml (1/2 pint) skimmed milk
1 tablespoon cornflour or sauce flour
1/2 teaspoon grated fresh nutmeg
25 g (1 oz) grated fresh parmesan
1 tablespoon dried breadcrumbs

1. Blanch the lasagne sheets in a large pan of boiling water, adding the sheets 1 at a time and stirring once or twice. Cook for 3 minutes, then drain and slip them into a bowl of cold water.
2. Make the filling. Heat a non-stick pan. When hot, add the oil and brown the mince, stirring until it is crumbly.
3. Add the garlic, onion, carrot and celery and cook for about 5 minutes until softened. Stir in the chopped tomatoes, purée, herbs and seasoning. Bring to the boil, then simmer for 12–15 minutes until the liquid has reduced a little.
4. Meanwhile, put the milk and flour into another pan and bring it slowly to the boil, whisking until thickened. Season well. Add the nutmeg. Simmer briefly, then remove from the heat.
5. Drain the pasta and pat it dry with kitchen paper.
6. Put a third of the meat in the base of a heatproof dish; cover it with 3 sheets of pasta. Trickle half the sauce over and sprinkle with half the parmesan. Add another third of meat, then the remaining pasta, the rest of the meat and the last of the sauce and parmesan. Scatter the breadcrumbs over.
7. You can cook the lasagne under the grill or in the oven. Either preheat the grill to a steady medium heat or preheat the oven to Gas Mark 5/190°C/375°F.
8. If using the grill, brown the lasagne top until bubbling and golden. If using the oven, bake for 25 minutes.

Points per serving: 5
Total Points per recipe: 20

Spicy Pork Casserole

Serves: 4

Preparation time: 15 minutes + 45–60 minutes cooking

Calories per serving: 230

Freezing: recommended

Pork is a good lean meat and full of flavour. Leg meat is the leanest, but shoulder pork cooks until meltingly tender. Delicious served with boiled rice, potatoes or pasta, but remember to add the extra Points.

500 g (1 lb 5 oz) lean boneless pork, cubed
2 teaspoons sunflower oil
1 onion, sliced
1 red pepper, cored and sliced
1 large leek, sliced
1 fat garlic clove, crushed
1 teaspoon sweet paprika
1 teaspoon mild curry powder
1 tablespoon plain flour
200 g (7 oz) canned chopped tomatoes
1/2 teaspoon sugar
1 teaspoon grated orange or lemon zest (optional but nice)
1 bay leaf
salt and freshly ground black pepper

1. Heat a non-stick frying-pan. When it is hot, add the meat and dry-fry it until brown. Remove and add the oil to the pan along with the onion, red pepper, leek and garlic plus 1–2 tablespoons water. Cover and cook gently for 5 minutes until softened.
2. Sprinkle in the spices and cook for a minute, then stir in the flour and cook for another minute.
3. Add the tomatoes, sugar, citrus zest, bay leaf, seasoning and about 300 ml (1/2 pint) water. Bring to the boil, stirring, then return the meat to the pan and mix it in. Cover and simmer for 45–60 minutes until tender.

Points per serving: 2 1/2
Total Points per recipe: 10 1/2

Light Potato Bake

Serves: 4

Preparation time: 15 minutes
+ 1 hour baking + 10 minutes
cooling
Calories per serving: with
stock 140; with milk 180

Freezing: recommended

Thinly sliced potatoes and
onions make good family
fillers and they needn't be
smothered in cream, butter
and cheese to be delicious.
Here is a lighter version that
is bound to please. For extra
flavour and nutrition, leave
the potatoes unpeeled.

500 g (1lb 2 oz) baking-style
  potatoes, scrubbed or peeled
  if desired
low-fat cooking spray
1 large onion, sliced thinly
500 ml (18 fl oz) hot vegetable
  stock (made with a stock
  cube)
or 500 ml (18 fl oz) skimmed
  milk, scalded
2 teaspoons low-fat spread
a little grated fresh nutmeg
  (optional)
salt and freshly ground black
  pepper

1. Slice the potatoes as thinly as possible. You can use the slicing
blade of a food processor or a mandolin for this.
2. Spray the inside of an ovenproof pie dish (about 1.5 litres/2
3/4 pints) with the cooking spray and place the dish on a baking
tray. Preheat the oven to Gas Mark 4/180°C/350°F.
3. Layer the potato and onion slices in the dish, seasoning well in
between. Slowly pour over the stock or milk and press the potato
slices under the liquid. Dot with the low-fat spread and sprinkle
the nutmeg over, if using.
4. Bake for about 1 hour until the top is golden brown, the liquid
absorbed and the potato cooked. Allow to stand for 10 minutes
before serving.

Points per serving: with milk 2; with stock 1½
Total Points per recipe: with milk 8½; with stock 6½

Eggs and Oven Chips with Tomato Salsa

Serves: 4

Preparation time: 15 minutes
+ 15 minutes cooking + ½
hour marinating
Calories per serving: 275

Freezing: not recommended

Egg and chips can be such a
treat. If fried they will be very
high in fat and Points, so cook
them in the oven instead.
And, instead of serving them
with the usual ketchup, try
a speedy, fresh salsa for a
Mexican kick.

500 g (1 lb 2 oz) reduced-fat
  thick-cut oven chips
low-fat cooking spray
4 free-range eggs
salt and freshly ground black
  pepper
For the salsa:
2 ripe tomatoes, chopped finely
1 small onion, grated
½ teaspoon salt
a good pinch each of ground
  cumin, ground coriander and
  ground garlic
1 teaspoon balsamic or red
  wine vinegar
1 tablespoon chopped fresh
  parsley or coriander

1. First, make the salsa. Mix the chopped tomatoes and onion with
the salt, flavourings, vinegar and fresh herbs. Leave for ½ hour for
the flavours to develop.
2. Preheat the oven according to the chip packet instructions,
normally Gas Mark 6/200°C/400°F. Cook the chips according
to the instructions on the packet.
3. 15 minutes before the end of the cooking time, spray a flan dish
or tin (21–25cm/8–10 inches diameter) or an ovenproof cast-iron
frying-pan, with low-fat cooking spray. Immediately crack the eggs
into the pan. Season and bake, uncovered, until lightly set – about
15 minutes.
4. Serve the eggs and chips with the salsa.

Points per serving: 4
Total Points per recipe: 16

Something Special

Here are a number of easy meals that are a touch exotic, but will still appeal to most palates. There are some familiar curries, Chinese classics and Italian, French and Mexican dishes – a veritable cook's tour!

Madras Fish Curry with Parsley Basmati

Serves: 4

Preparation time: 15 minutes
+ 25 minutes cooking
Calories per serving: 345

Freezing: recommended

Top with chopped cucumber and tomato, and a little fresh mint.

1 onion, chopped finely
2 garlic cloves, crushed
1 large fresh green chilli, de-seeded and chopped
2 teaspoons ginger purée
2 teaspoons sunflower oil
2–3 teaspoons medium or strong curry powder mix
a few dashes of hot pepper sauce (optional)
200 g (7 oz) canned chopped tomatoes
125 g (4½ oz) garden peas, thawed if frozen
100 g (3½ oz) peeled prawns, thawed if frozen
300 g (10 oz) white fish fillet, e.g. cod or haddock, skinned and cubed
200 g (7 oz) basmati rice
2 tablespoons chopped fresh parsley
1 teaspoon black poppy seeds
salt and freshly ground black pepper

1. Put the onion, garlic, chilli and ginger into a saucepan and stir in the oil with 2 tablespoons of water. Heat until the pan starts to sizzle, then cover and cook gently for about 10 minutes until softened.
2. Add the curry, then cook for 1–2 minutes. Add a few dashes of pepper sauce if using.
3. Stir in 200 ml (7 fl oz) cold water, the tomatoes and seasoning. Bring to the boil. Partially cover and simmer for 10 minutes.
4. Add the peas, then the prawns and cubes of fish, stirring gently so as not to break them up. Season, then simmer for 5–7 minutes until the fish just feels firm. Set aside to stand while you cook the rice.
5. Put a large pan of lightly salted water on to boil. Stir in the rice, return to the boil, then simmer for 8 minutes from the time the water returns to the boil. Drain the rice in a large sieve or colander and leave it to sit for 5 minutes. Check the rice for seasoning and gently stir in the parsley. Sprinkle the poppy seeds over. Serve the curry and rice together.

Points per serving: 4
Total Points per recipe: with cod 19½; with haddock 19

Lamb and Spinach Korma

Serves: 4

Preparation time: 20 minutes
+ 30 minutes cooking
Calories per serving: 305

Freezing: recommended

This is nice with plain boiled basmati rice and a teaspoon of mango chutney.

2 tablespoons desiccated coconut
400 g (14 oz) lean cubed lamb, trimmed of all fat
1 large onion, halved
1 fat garlic clove, crushed
1 large fresh green chilli, de-seeded (optional)
2 teaspoons ginger purée (optional)
low-fat cooking spray
2 teaspoons sunflower oil
2 teaspoons korma paste
200 g (7 oz) young spinach leaves
2 tablespoons Bio low-fat plain yogurt
salt and freshly ground black pepper

1. Steep the coconut in 300 ml (½ pint) boiling water for 30 minutes, then strain and reserve the water. Discard the coconut.
2. Trim excess fat from the neck fillets and cut into 1 cm (½ inch) thick medallions. In a food processor, blend together half the onion, the garlic, chilli and ginger. Chop the remaining onion half.
3. Heat a non-stick frying-pan until quite hot and spray lightly with the low-fat cooking spray. Brown the lamb medallions for about 3 minutes, then remove them with a slotted spoon.
4. Add the oil to the pan and reheat. Gently sauté the chopped onion for about 5 minutes adding 1–2 tablespoons of water if the pan looks dry. Stir in the fresh spice mixture plus the korma paste and cook for another 2 minutes.
5. Return the lamb to the pan. Pour in the coconut water. Season well, bring to the boil, partially cover and simmer gently for 20–25 minutes, stirring occasionally until the meat is tender.
6. Stir in the spinach and cook for a few minutes until wilted. Check the seasoning and serve topped with the yogurt.

Points per serving: 5½
Total Points per recipe: 21½

Italian Seafood Pasta

Serves: 4

Preparation and cooking time:
25 minutes
Calories per serving: with
seafood cocktail 310; with
prawns 320

Freezing: not recommended

A lovely light dish for when
you want to treat the family
to a Mediterranean meal.
Many supermarket frozen fish
cabinets contain packs of
frozen seafood mix; otherwise
use frozen peeled prawns.
Serve with a crisp green salad
dressed with a little fresh
lemon juice and chopped fresh
parsley.

200 g (7 oz) green tagliatelle
1 fat garlic clove, crushed
1 small onion, sliced thinly
2 teaspoons olive oil
2 tablespoons dry vermouth or
   white wine or dry sherry
2 tomatoes, chopped
300 g (10 oz) frozen seafood
   cocktail mix or peeled
   prawns, thawed
2 tablespoons half-fat crème
   fraîche
a good pinch of dried basil or
   oregano
salt and freshly ground black
   pepper

1. Boil the pasta according to the packet instructions, then drain
and rinse it in cold water and drain again.
2. Meanwhile, put the garlic, onion and oil in a large saucepan and
heat until sizzling. Add 1–2 tablespoons of water, and cover and
cook for 3 minutes over a gentle heat until the onion is softened.
3. Mix in the vermouth, wine or sherry and tomatoes and cook for
another 3 minutes.
4. Pat the thawed seafood dry with kitchen paper, if necessary, and
tip into the pot. Heat for about 2 minutes until piping hot, then
mix in the crème fraîche and herbs. Heat again.
5. Season the sauce to taste, then toss in the cooked pasta and
reheat well.

Points per serving: 4
Total Points per recipe: with seafood cocktail 15; with prawns 16

Chicken Fajitas

Serves: 4

Preparation time: 10 minutes
+ 15 minutes cooking + 1/2
hour marinating
Calories per serving: 275

Freezing: not recommended

If you enjoy fun finger food,
then you'll certainly like
eating fajitas. You'll need a
packet of soft wheat tortillas
that look like pancakes. These
are available in plain, garlic or
coriander flavour. Use a lean
chicken breast for this recipe.
The traditional high-fat
avocado is replaced by thinly
sliced cucumber.

1/2 cucumber, sliced wafer-thin
4 medium soft wheat tortillas,
   plain or garlic flavoured
2 skinless, boneless chicken
   breasts, about 200 g (7 oz)
   weight
1 teaspoon olive or sunflower
   oil mixed with 1/2 teaspoon
   mild chilli powder and 1/2
   teaspoon ground cumin
low-fat cooking spray
1 tablespoon chopped fresh
   parsley or coriander or mint
2 ripe tomatoes, chopped
4 tablespoons very-low-fat plain
   fromage frais
salt and freshly ground black
   pepper

1. Layer the cucumber in a colander, sprinkling each layer lightly
with salt. Leave for 1/2 hour to soften, then rinse and pat dry
with kitchen paper. (This is necessary to enable the fajitas to be
rolled easily.)
2. Warm the tortillas according to the packet instructions – either
in foil in a warm oven or in the microwave.
3. Slice the chicken into strips, then mix it with the spicy oil and
seasoning. Leave for 5 minutes or so while you prepare the rest of
the ingredients.
4. When ready to cook, heat a large non-stick pan and spray it
lightly with low-fat cooking spray. Cook the chicken strips, stirring
them occasionally until browned and just firm.
5. Mix the cucumber with the fresh herb of your choice. Lay the
tortillas out on a board and scatter the cucumber and tomatoes
over them. Top with the chicken strips and drizzle over the fromage
frais. Roll them up and eat quickly.

Points per serving: 4 1/2
Total Points per recipe: 19

Easy Moussaka

Serves: 4

Preparation time: 25 minutes
+ 30 minutes cooking
Calories per serving: with
lamb 310; with beef 285

Freezing: recommended

Moussakas can be quite high
in fat if the aubergines are
fried in oil – they can soak up
such a lot. The solution is to
blanch them in boiling water,
then drain them well. Use
plain yogurt for the topping,
it's light and tangy.

1 aubergine, about 250 g (9 oz)
   weight
400 g (14 oz) lean minced lamb
   or beef
1 large onion, chopped finely
a fat garlic clove, crushed
425 g (15 oz) canned chopped
   tomatoes
a good pinch of dried dill or
   oregano or mixed herbs
2 tablespoons chopped fresh
   parsley (optional)
salt and freshly ground black
   pepper
For the topping:
1 large free-range egg
2 teaspoons plain flour
200 g (7 oz) carton low-fat
   plain yogurt
2 tablespoons dried
   breadcrumbs

1. Slice the aubergine into 5 mm (1/4 inch) discs. Bring a pan of
lightly salted water to the boil. Drop in the aubergine slices and
blanch for a minute or so until just softened. Drain them well,
then pat them dry with kitchen paper. Set aside.
2. Heat a non-stick frying-pan. When it is quite hot, dry-fry the
mince, adding it in stages and stirring well until it is crumbly and
browned. Remove the mince with a slotted spoon and drain it on
kitchen paper.
3. Put the onion, garlic and canned tomatoes into the frying-pan.
Bring to the boil, then simmer very gently for 10 minutes until the
onion softens. Stir in the browned mince and cook for another 5
minutes, adding the dried herbs and seasoning. Remove and stir in
the fresh parsley, if using. Tip into a shallow ovenproof pie dish and
cover with the aubergine slices.
4. Beat the egg, flour, yogurt and seasoning and spoon the topping
over the aubergines. Sprinkle the breadcrumbs over. Set aside for a
few minutes while you preheat the oven to Gas Mark 4/180°C/350°F.
5. Place the dish on a baking tray and bake for about 30 minutes
until the top is golden brown and bubbling. Cool for 10 minutes
before serving.

Points per serving: with lamb 6; with beef 5
Total Points per recipe: with lamb 25 1/2; with beef 20

Veal Escalopes with Neapolitan (Tomato) Sauce

Serves: 4

Preparation time: 20 minutes
+ 20 minutes cooking
Calories per serving: with veal
165; with pork 180

Freezing: recommended

Delicious with pasta or rice
and a helping of green beans
or mange-tout peas. Add the
additional Points for the
pasta or rice.

4 veal or pork escalopes, about
   100 g (3 1/2 oz) each
6 fresh tomatoes
1 onion, sliced thinly

1 fat garlic clove, crushed
1 small green, red or yellow
   pepper, cored and sliced thinly
2 teaspoons olive oil
1 sprig fresh thyme or 1/4
   teaspoon dried thyme
2 tablespoons dry white wine
   (optional)
low-fat cooking spray
salt and freshly ground black
   pepper
For the topping (optional):
2 tablespoons chopped fresh
   parsley
1 teaspoon grated fresh lemon
   zest

1. The escalopes should ideally be beaten thin. To do this, place
them between 2 sheets of baking parchment or wet greaseproof
paper, 1 at a time, and beat them with a rolling pin. (Not essential
but it makes them look more authentic.) Set aside.
2. Skin the tomatoes. Remove the core with the tip of a sharp knife
and score the other end in a cross. Place in a heatproof dish and
cover with boiling water. Leave for a minute, then drain them
carefully in a colander and hold under cold running water for a
few moments. Slip off the skin and chop the flesh.
3. Put the onion, garlic and pepper slices in a saucepan. Stir in the
oil and 2 tablespoons of water. Heat the pan until it sizzles, then
cover and simmer for about 5 minutes until softened.
4. Add the tomatoes, thyme, wine (if using) and seasoning. Bring
to the boil, then cover and simmer for 10 minutes, stirring once or
twice. Uncover for the last 3 minutes or so.
5. Now cook the escalopes. They take just a few minutes. Heat
a non-stick frying-pan. When hot, spray it lightly with low-fat
cooking spray. Cook the escalopes for 2–3 minutes on each side or
until they feel just firm. Season them in the pan. Do not overcook
or they will become tough.
6. Serve the escalopes with the fresh tomato sauce spooned over
and the optional toppings, if using.

Points per serving: with veal 4; with pork 2
Total Points per recipe: with veal 16; with pork 8

Cantonese Sweet and Sour Beef and Green Pepper

Serves: 4

Preparation time: 15 minutes + 10 minutes cooking
Calories per serving: with sirloin 200; with rump 190

Freezing: not recommended

If you love sweet and sour, then why not make up a fresh recipe instead of using a can or jar? It's so easy to cook and just as nice as a good take-away meal. Serve with plain boiled rice – remember to add the extra Points.

2 lean sirloin steaks or 1 rump steak, about 400 g (14 oz) total weight
2 teaspoons sunflower oil
1 fat garlic clove, crushed
1–2 teaspoons ginger purée (optional)
2 salad onions, chopped
1 green pepper, de-seeded and cut into 1 cm (1/2 inch) squares
2 pineapple rings, fresh or canned in juice (not syrup), chopped

For the sauce:
4 tablespoons pineapple juice (can be natural juice from the can)
1 tablespoon dry sherry (optional)
2 tablespoons soy sauce
2 teaspoons white wine vinegar
1 teaspoon caster sugar
2 teaspoons cornflour

1. First, mix all the sauce ingredients together and set aside in a small jug.
2. Trim the visible fat from the meat and cut it into thin strips. Mix it with the oil so it is well coated. Heat a non-stick wok until you can feel a good steady heat rising. Toss in the steak, stir-frying for about 2 minutes until nicely browned.
3. Add the garlic, ginger (if using), onions and pepper and stir-fry for another 2 minutes.
4. Add the pineapple pieces, then pour in the sauce and mix well until it starts to bubble and thicken. Simmer for 1 minute, then serve immediately.

Points per serving: 4 1/2
Total Points per recipe: with sirloin 18 1/2; with rump 18

Vegetable and Chickpea Couscous

Serves: 4

Preparation time: 15 minutes
+ cooling + 15 minutes
cooking
Calories per serving: 330

Freezing: recommended

Couscous is a speciality
of North Africa. It is a
pre-cooked paste of wheat
semolina rolled into tiny
grains. For ease, buy the
instant grain.

200 g (7 oz) instant couscous
1/2 teaspoon salt
1 onion, chopped
1 green pepper, cored and
    chopped
1 fat garlic clove, crushed
1 celery stick, sliced
2 teaspoons olive or sunflower
    oil
1 teaspoon ground cumin
1 teaspoon ground coriander
1/2 teaspoon ground cinnamon
grated zest of 1 small lemon
425 g (15 oz) canned chopped
    tomatoes
1 large bay leaf
425g (15 oz) canned chickpeas
    (reserve the can juice)
1–2 tablespoons chopped fresh
    parsley or coriander
    (optional)
salt and freshly ground black
    pepper

1. Tip the couscous into a measuring jug and note the volume.
Pour it into a bowl, then add the same volume of boiling water plus
the salt. Stir well to mix and leave to cool, stirring the grains once
or twice. When cold, spread the grains on a clean tray and, using
clean hands, rub the grains free of any lumps. This is a lovely job –
very satisfying! Set the couscous aside.
2. Make the stew. Put the onion, green pepper, garlic, celery and
oil into a heavy-based saucepan with 2 tablespoons of water. Heat
until it all starts to sizzle, then stir and cover. Cook on low heat for
about 5 minutes until softened.
3. Add the spices and the lemon zest, and cook for a minute. Then
mix in the tomatoes, bay leaf, chickpeas and the can juice. Season
and bring to the boil, then cover and simmer for 10 minutes.
4. Reheat the couscous either in a covered bowl in the microwave
or a saucepan, stirring often to prevent the grains from sticking.
Serve the stew over the couscous garnished with parsley or coriander
if desired.

Points per serving: 5
Total Points per recipe: 20

Orange-Glazed Gammon with Sweet Potato Mash

Serves: 4

Preparation time: 15 minutes
+ 20 minutes cooking
Calories per serving: 270

Freezing: recommended

Gammon seems to have gone
slightly out of fashion, which
is a pity as it is so tasty and
lean. At the end of cooking,
swirling a little fresh orange
juice and honey in the pan
makes a delicious sauce. Sweet
potatoes are easy to buy now
and look like red-skinned
spuds. If you don't like sweet
potatoes though, serve this
with ordinary mash. For a
green vegetable accompaniment,
try curly kale or cabbage.

2 sweet potatoes, about 250 g
    (9 oz) each
1 teaspoon salt
1 teaspoon low-fat spread
a little freshly grated nutmeg
    (optional)
4 gammon steaks, about 100 g
    (3 1/2 oz) each, or 2 larger
    ones, halved
low-fat cooking spray
juice of 1 orange
1 teaspoon clear honey
salt and freshly ground black
    pepper

1. Peel the sweet potatoes and cut them into cubes. Cover them
with cold water, add 1 teaspoon of salt and boil gently for 10–15
minutes until tender. Drain, reserving a small cupful of water.
Mash well using a potato masher, Add the low-fat spread, nutmeg
to taste, if desired, and a small trickle of the reserved water to make
it smooth, if necessary. Keep warm.
2. Snip the edges of the gammon steaks – this stops them from
curling during cooking. Trim off any excess fat.
3. Heat a large non-stick frying-pan. When you can feel a steady
heat rising, spray the surface lightly with low-fat cooking spray.
4. Add the steaks and cook for about 5 minutes on each side until
tender. Pour in the juice and honey; bubble until syrupy and
reduced down. Season with pepper. Serve with the hot sweet potato.

Points per serving: 4
Total Points per recipe: 15 1/2

Mushroom Risotto

Serves: 4

Preparation time: 10 minutes
+ 20 minutes cooking
Calories per serving: 285

Freezing: recommended

Risotto is a speciality of
northern Italy where it is
almost as popular as pasta and
eaten nearly every day. It is
wonderful comfort food. You
need a special stubby rice
grain that cooks to a delicious
creaminess, but the dish
doesn't have to be high in fat,
which makes it ideal when
you are watching your Points.
For best results use arborio
risotto grain, on sale in most
supermarkets.

250 g (9 oz) button mushrooms
1 tablespoon light soy sauce
1 onion, chopped finely
1 fat garlic clove, crushed
2 teaspoons olive oil
250 g (9 oz) risotto rice,
    preferably arborio
3 tablespoons dry white wine
    (optional)
1 litre (1¾ pint) hot vegetable
    or chicken stock
1 tablespoon grated fresh
    parmesan
salt and freshly ground black
    pepper
1 tablespoon chopped fresh
    parsley, to garnish (optional)

1. Halve the mushrooms if they are large, then place them in a
saucepan with about 4 tablespoons of water and the soy sauce.
Mix together well, then cover and cook on very gentle heat for
5–10 minutes or until softened. Season to taste and set aside with
any juice that has formed.
2. In a large, heavy-based saucepan, put the onion, garlic, oil and
2 tablespoons of water. Heat until it starts to sizzle, then cover and
cook on low heat for about 5 minutes until softened.
3. Uncover and stir in the risotto rice and wine, if using. Cook for
about 2 minutes so the grains become opaque. Pour in a quarter of
the stock and bring to the boil, stirring.
4. When the stock has been absorbed, stir in about a cupful more
and cook until absorbed. Continue like this, adding a little stock
after each amount has been absorbed until most of the stock has
been used or until the rice has become tender and creamy. The
total cooking time should be around 18–20 minutes. At the end
there should still be a little firmness to the grain.
5. Mix in the mushrooms and any juice, and finally the parmesan.
Serve immediately, sprinkled with the parsley, if liked.

Points per serving: 4
Total Points per recipe: 16½

Roasted Roots and Shoots with Griddled Tofu

Serves: 4

Preparation time: 15 minutes
+ 35 minutes cooking
Calories per serving: 185

Freezing: recommended

If you are vegetarian, there is
no need to miss out on roasts
and grills. Lots of vegetables
take on a delicious flavour
when roasted and you can
grill firm tofu to a nice crisp
coating. If you can find them,
use roasting bags for the
vegetables – they keep the
juices but allow browning.

1 large red onion, quartered
4 whole garlic cloves, unpeeled
1 red pepper, quartered and
    cored
1 yellow pepper, quartered and
    cored
2 carrots, peeled and halved
2 courgettes, topped, tailed and
    halved
1 small fennel bulb, quartered,
    or 2 celery sticks, halved
low-fat cooking spray – olive oil
    or garlic flavoured
1 teaspoon dried mixed herbs
1 small lemon (optional)
2 × 200 g (7 oz) blocks of
    smoked or marinated tofu
a few shakes of soy sauce
salt and freshly ground black
    pepper

1. Preheat the oven to Gas Mark 5/190°C/375°F. Put all the prepared
vegetables into a large food bag or roasting bag. Spray with about
5 bursts of the low-fat spray, add the dried herbs and some seasoning
to taste, then shake or stir well together to mix.
2. If using a roasting bag, simply place it on a roasting pan.
Otherwise, spread the vegetables directly on to the pan. Cook for
about 30 minutes, stirring or shaking once or twice to cook evenly.
Watch the peppers don't overcook. The vegetables are ready when
they can be lightly pierced with the tip of a knife. Remove and
allow them to cool while you cook the tofu. They can be sprinkled
with a little fresh lemon juice as they cool.
3. For the tofu, cut each block into four. Heat a non-stick ridged
griddle or heavy-based frying-pan. When quite hot, spray it lightly
with the low-fat cooking spray.
4. Cook the tofu for about 3 minutes on each side until nicely
browned and slightly crisp. Turn them with a palette knife so as
not to disturb the crust that forms. Shake a little soy sauce over
and serve the tofu with the vegetables.

Points per serving: 1
Total Points per recipe: 4

Main-Course Salads

Salads are great for preparing ahead and require virtually no cooking. They can also be very satisfying and make excellent main meals. However, you still have to count Calories and Points when eating salads because dressings made with oils, mayonnaise and creams can be high in fats. Fortunately there are many virtually fat-free alternative ingredients such as yogurts, lemons, mustard and even water that you can use to dress your dishes. One thing to remember is to season salads well; cold food needs extra flavour.

Ham (or Red Bean) Waldorf

Serves: 2

Preparation time: 15 minutes
+ 1 hour softening
Calories per serving: with ham
100; with beans 120

Freezing: not recommended

Ⓥ if making red bean version

This much-loved celery, apple and cabbage salad is versatile – you can add various protein foods to make it a main-meal dish. If you want to add the traditional walnuts then add another ¹/₂ Point per serving.

1 Granny Smith apple, cored
   and sliced thinly
1 tablespoon fresh lemon juice
2 celery sticks, sliced thinly
¹/₄ small red cabbage, cored and
   sliced thinly
1 large salad onion, chopped
2 thin slices ham, cut in strips
   or 2 heaped tablespoons
   canned red kidney beans
1 punnet salad cress, snipped
salt and freshly ground black
   pepper
For the dressing:
1 tablespoon low-fat
   mayonnaise
1 tablespoon low-fat plain
   yogurt
1 tablespoon skimmed milk

1. Toss the apple slices in the lemon juice, then mix them with the celery, cabbage and onion in a bowl. Season well and toss together, then cover and leave for an hour.
2. Mix the dressing ingredients in a cup, then pour the dressing into the prepared salad ingredients and mix well. Set aside for another hour, this time in the fridge.
3. When ready to serve, mix in the ham or beans. Garnish with the cress to serve.

Points per serving: with ham 2; with beans 1¹/₂
Total Points per recipe: with ham 3¹/₂; with beans 2¹/₂

Arabian Chicken Salad (Chicken with Carrot, Cucumber and Mint)

Serves: 4

Preparation time: 15 minutes
Calories per serving: 135

Freezing: not recommended

A sunny salad reminiscent of the Middle East which is ideal for a light summer lunch. You can use ready-cooked chicken breasts for this, but do skin them first.

¹/₂ cucumber, halved
   lengthways
2 carrots, cut in wafer-thin slices
2 large salad onions, chopped
2 medium cooked, boneless
   chicken breasts, skinned and
   shredded
salt and freshly ground black
   pepper
lettuce leaves, to serve
For the dressing:
2 tablespoons low-fat plain
   yogurt
2 tablespoons fresh lemon juice
2 tablespoons chopped fresh
   mint or 1 teaspoon dried
   mint

1. Scoop the seeds from the cucumber with a teaspoon, then slice thinly.
2. Mix with the carrots and onions. Season lightly and set aside for an hour for the flavour to develop.
3. Mix the dressing ingredients together, then blend into the vegetables and finally add the chicken. Check the seasoning and serve on a bed of lettuce leaves.

Points per serving: 1¹/₂
Total Points per recipe: 5¹/₂

Tuna and Corn Salad in Lettuce Cups

Serves: 2

Preparation time: 15 minutes
Calories per serving: 130

Freezing: not recommended

Whole leaves of Iceberg or
Webb's Wonder lettuces make
good containers for serving
salads. This should be a
popular mixture.

100 g (3½ oz) canned
  sweetcorn, drained
¼ small onion, chopped finely
1 tomato, chopped finely
1 tablespoon very-low-fat plain
  fromage frais
a good squeeze of fresh lemon
  juice
100 g (3½ oz) canned tuna in
  brine, drained and flaked
2 large cup-shaped leaves of
  Iceberg or another crisp
  lettuce
salt and freshly ground black
  pepper
½ punnet salad cress, to serve

1. Mix the sweetcorn, onion and tomato together. Then make the
dressing by beating the fromage frais and lemon juice with some
seasoning.
2. Stir the dressing into the vegetables and fold in the flaked tuna.
Spoon into the lettuce leaves. Serve scattered with some cress.

Points per serving: 1½
Total Points per recipe: 2½

Italian Bread and Tomato (Panzanella)

Serves: 4

Preparation time: 15 minutes
+ 2 hours chilling
Calories per serving: 180

Freezing: not recommended

You need country-style bread
for this, cut in thick slices.
A light rye, a stale ciabatta or
a multi-grain loaf would be
ideal – adjust the Points as
necessary. The juices of the
tomato moisten the bread and
make their own dressing.

200 g (7 oz) whole country-
  style bread, sliced
2 ripe beef tomatoes
1 fat fresh garlic clove, chopped
  finely
1 small red onion, sliced thinly
  and soaked in cold water for
  1 hour
3 or 4 large fresh basil leaves,
  torn, according to taste
salt and freshly ground black
  pepper

1. Dip the bread slices briefly into a bowl of cold water and squeeze
them dry, then break them up and place them in the base of a
salad bowl.
2. Remove the core from the tomatoes with the tip of a sharp knife
and slice them thinly. Layer the tomato slices on top of the bread,
seasoning well between slices and adding the garlic, onion and
torn basil as you make the layers.
3. Finish with a little seasoning. Cover with clingfilm and store
in the fridge for 2 hours or so to allow the juices to soak into the
bread. Toss everything together to serve.

Points per serving: 1½
Total Points per recipe: 6½

Cook's note:
In Italy this salad is served with thinly sliced mozzarella. You could
use 100 g (3½ oz) half-fat mozzarella and add 1 Point per serving.

Leek and Egg Mimosa

Serves: 2

Preparation and cooking time: 15 minutes

Calories per serving: 150

Freezing: not recommended

This is a simple salad to make yet it looks really appetising. The main ingredients are leeks and eggs combined with a light dressing. Good as a light meal or an accompaniment to cold chicken or salmon.

2 leeks, washed and sliced thinly
2 hard-boiled eggs, chopped finely
2 tablespoons chopped fresh chives
For the dressing:
2 teaspoons olive or sunflower oil
1 tablespoon white wine vinegar
$1/2$ teaspoon clear honey
$1/2$ teaspoon French mustard
salt and freshly ground black pepper

1. Boil the leek slices for about 2 minutes in lightly salted water then drain and cool them under cold running water for a minute or so. Drain them again. Ideally, pat them dry with kitchen paper.
2. Shake the dressing ingredients together in a clean jam jar or whisk them together until blended. Toss the dressing into the leeks, season well and allow to marinate for an hour. Tip into a shallow serving bowl and top with the egg and chives. Serve with crusty French bread – remember to add the extra Points.

Points per serving: 2$1/2$
Total Points per recipe: 5

Thai Prawn Salad

Serves: 4

Preparation time: 15 minutes + 30 minutes marinating

Calories per serving: 65

Freezing: not recommended

Many supermarkets sell uncooked tiger prawns that just need shelling before cooking. They are nicest marinated for a short period in a spicy dressing before quick stir-frying and tossing into a salad. If you can't find raw prawns, use thawed frozen peeled prawns and reheat them in the marinade. Hot prawns create an exciting contrast to the chilled salad.

250 g (9 oz) raw tiger prawns, thawed if frozen
1 carrot
1 small Cos or Romaine lettuce, shredded
$1/4$ cucumber, sliced thinly
1 tablespoon chopped fresh coriander (optional, but nice)
1 tablespoon chopped fresh basil (optional, but nice)
low-fat cooking spray
2 tablespoons light soy sauce
freshly ground black pepper
For the marinade:
juice of 1 lime or $1/2$ lemon
1 tablespoon Thai fish sauce or light soy sauce
2 garlic cloves, crushed
1 plump fresh red chilli, de-seeded and chopped, or $1/2$ teaspoon mild chilli powder

1. Peel the shells and legs from the prawns. Leave on the tails (for appearance) or remove them (for ease of eating).
2. Whisk the marinade ingredients together and toss them into the prawns. Leave for about 30 minutes to marinate.
3. Using a swivel vegetable peeler, cut the carrot into long thin ribbons. If you prefer, you could coarsely grate the carrot. Mix with the lettuce, cucumber and fresh herbs, if using, and chill until ready to serve.
4. To serve, heat a non-stick wok. When you can feel a steady heat rising, spray the surface lightly with low-fat cooking spray. Immediately add in the prawns and all the marinade and toss until the prawns are firm and pink.
5. Meanwhile, dress the salad with the 2 tablespoons of soy sauce, season and finally toss in the hot prawns and any pan juices. When well dressed, serve quickly.

Points per serving: 1
Total Points per recipe: 4

Courgette and Pepper Salad

Serves: 2

Preparation time: 15 minutes
+ 1 hour soaking + marinating
Calories per serving: 85

Freezing: not recommended

This is a good salad for a light lunch or as an accompaniment for grills or omelettes. Lots of sunny Mediterranean flavours here. This is good served with crusty bread to mop up the delicious juices, but remember to add the extra Points for the bread.

1 small red onion, peeled and
  chopped
1 large courgette, topped and
  tailed, then grated coarsely
1 small green pepper, cored
  and chopped
2 ripe tomatoes, quartered,
  de-seeded and sliced in strips
salt and freshly ground black
  pepper
For the dressing:
1 tablespoon fresh lemon juice
2 teaspoons olive oil
1 tablespoon chopped fresh
  parsley

1. For a milder flavour, soak the chopped onion in cold water for an hour, then drain.
2. Mix the onion with the rest of the vegetables and season well.
3. Whisk or shake the dressing ingredients together with 1 tablespoon of water and toss into the vegetables.
4. Cover and leave for about 1 hour to marinate before serving.

Points per serving: 1
Total Points per recipe: 2

Feeling Fit and Fresh Chef's Salad

Serves: 2

Preparation time: 20 minutes
Calories per serving: for base
salad 165

Freezing: not recommended

There's no definitive recipe for a chef's salad. The idea is that whatever a chef has left in his fridge, he tosses together with salad leaves and dressing.

For the base salad:
2 Little Gem lettuces, shredded
1 large salad onion, chopped
1 packet of prepared watercress
  leaves
6–8 cherry tomatoes, halved
1 carrot, grated coarsely, or 4
  large radishes, sliced
2 teaspoons olive oil
1 tablespoon white wine vinegar
1 tablespoon apple juice or water
a good pinch of caster sugar
1 portion low-fat croûtons (see
  Cook's note)

salt and freshly ground black
  pepper
Choose 2 ingredients from:
- 40 g (1½ oz) half-fat Cheddar cheese or Edam cheese, grated or chopped: 55 Calories; with Cheddar 2½ Points, with Edam 3½ Points
- 100 g (3½ oz) canned tuna in brine, drained and flaked: 55 Calories; 1 Point
- 2 eggs, hard-boiled and chopped: 75 Calories; 3 Points
- 50 g (1¾ oz) lean ham, cut in strips: 25 Calories; with pre-packed ham 1 Point; with Parma ham 2 Points
- 75 g (2¾ oz) cooked chicken, shredded: 55 Calories; 2 Points
- 3 tablespoons canned red kidney beans: 25 Calories; 1 Point
- 2 tablespoons sunflower seeds: 90 Calories; 2 Points

1. Mix the lettuce, onion, watercress, tomatoes and carrot or radishes together in a big bowl. Whisk or shake together the oil, vinegar, apple juice or water, sugar and seasoning. Get the croûtons ready (see Cook's note).
2. Choose and prepare your toppings. When ready to serve, toss the salad with the dressing and divide between 2 plates. Add the toppings over the salad and scatter the croûtons over. Serve immediately.

Points per serving: for base salad 2
Total Points per recipe: for base salad 3½

Cook's note:
To make low-fat croûtons, cut the crust from 2 thick slices of white, brown or multi-grain bread. Spread the slices out in a roasting pan. Spray evenly and lightly with low-fat cooking spray, about 3 or 4 bursts. Heat the oven to Gas Mark 3/170°C/325°F and bake the bread cubes for 20–25 minutes until pale golden and firm. Don't over-crisp or they will be rock hard – they will crisp up on cooling. Makes 2 portions of 1½ Points each.

Two Side Salads

Each serves: 4

Preparation and cooking time:
For the Indian Carrot Salad and
Warm Green Bean and Cherry
Tomato Salad: 15 minutes each
+ 1/2–1 hour marinating
Calories per serving: for Indian
Carrot Salad 30; for Warm Green
Bean and Cherry Tomato
Salad 50

Freezing: not recommended

For the Indian Carrot Salad:
3 carrots, grated coarsely
juice of 1 large lemon
a pinch of caster sugar
1/2 teaspoon ground cumin
1 teaspoon ground coriander
1 tablespoon chopped fresh
    parsley, coriander or mint
1/2 teaspoon poppy seeds
salt and freshly ground black
    pepper

1. Put the carrots in a bowl. Whisk the lemon juice with the sugar, cumin and seasoning, and mix into the carrot along with the chopped herbs. Marinate for at least 1 hour, then serve sprinkled with the poppy seeds.

For the Warm Green Bean and Cherry Tomato Salad:
250 g (9 oz) cherry tomatoes
250 g (9 oz) whole green beans, topped, tailed and halved
salt and freshly ground black pepper
For the dressing:
1 tablespoon balsamic or red wine vinegar
2 teaspoons olive or sunflower oil
1 teaspoon Dijon or French mustard
1 tablespoon water
a pinch of caster sugar

1. Halve the cherry tomatoes and place them in a bowl. Whisk the dressing ingredients with a little seasoning and mix into the tomatoes. Leave for half an hour.
2. When ready to serve, boil the beans in enough lightly salted water to cover for about 4–5 minutes, then drain.
3. Toss the hot beans into the dressed tomatoes and serve.

Points per serving: for Indian Carrot Salad 0 Points; for Warm Green Bean and Cherry Tomato Salad 1/2 Point
Total Points per recipe: for Indian Carrot Salad 0 Points; for Warm Green Bean and Cherry Tomato Salad 2 Points

Two New Potato Salads

Serves: 4

Preparation time: 10 minutes
+ 20 minutes cooking + 15
minutes cooking
Calories per serving: with
Honey Mustard Dressing 175;
with Creamy Mayo Dressing
130

Freezing: not recommended

Ⓥ if making the creamy mayo version

Potato salad is always welcome at any dining or buffet table. The art of a good potato salad is to dress the vegetables while they cool after cooking. That way they absorb less dressing and are more tasty. Here are two variations.

500 g (1lb 2 oz) baby new
    potatoes, scrubbed
2 salad onions, chopped, or 1
    small red onion, sliced thinly
1–2 tablespoons fat-free
    dressing
salt and freshly ground black
    pepper
**For the Honey Mustard
Dressing:**
1 rasher lean back bacon,
    trimmed of fat and grilled or
    dry-fried until crisp
1 tablespoon balsamic or red
    wine vinegar
2 teaspoons sunflower oil
2 teaspoons coarse-grain
    mustard
2 teaspoons clear honey
**For the Creamy Mayo
Dressing:**
2 tablespoons low-fat
    mayonnaise
2 tablespoons skimmed milk
1 tablespoon chopped fresh
    parsley or fresh dill or 1/2
    teaspoon dried mixed herbs
    or dried dill weed

1. Boil the potatoes in lightly salted water for 12–15 minutes until just tender. Drain and cool them for 20 minutes, then toss in the onions, fat-free dressing and seasoning.
2. Choose your dressing. For the Honey Mustard Dressing, snip the bacon into small strips with scissors and mix them well with the remaining ingredients. For the Creamy Mayo Dressing, whisk the mayonnaise and milk until smooth and add the parsley, dill or mixed herbs.
3. When the potatoes are cool, add the dressing of your choice and serve.

Points per serving: with Honey Mustard Dressing 2 1/2;
with Creamy Mayo Dressing 2
Total Points per recipe: with Honey Mustard Dressing 10;
with Creamy Mayo Dressing 7

Desserts and Bakes

Sweet things don't need to be high in Points and Calories to be enjoyable. Fruits form the mainstay of these desserts, but you can have low-fat bakes that taste every bit as good as their fuller fat versions. In one case, we even replace the traditional fat with a fruit purée, retaining the moist texture. Most sweeteners cannot be heated, so if you serve hot desserts you will have to use sugar (if you need it for taste).

Apple Batter Cake

Serves: 6

Preparation time: 15 minutes
+ 1–1¼ hours baking
Calories per serving: 225

Freezing: recommended

The French call this a *clafoutis* – and traditionally it includes lots of butter. This is a lighter version. Serve warm and fresh from the oven with dollops of fat-free fromage frais.

low-fat cooking spray
75 g (2¾ oz) self-raising flour
1 teaspoon baking powder
¼ teaspoon ground cinnamon
125 g (4½ oz) caster sugar
100 ml (3½ fl oz) skimmed milk
1 tablespoon sunflower oil
2 eggs, beaten
25 g (1 oz) light soft brown sugar
500 g (1 lb 2 oz) Granny Smith apples, cored and sliced thinly
1 teaspoon icing sugar, to serve

1. Line the base of a 20 cm (8 inch) round shallow cake tin with baking parchment and lightly spray the sides with low-fat cooking spray. Preheat the oven to Gas Mark 4/180°C/350°F.
2. Put all the ingredients except the soft brown sugar, apples and icing sugar into a food processor or blender and whizz until smooth.
3. Sprinkle the soft brown sugar over the cake tin base, then scatter the apples over in an even layer. Pour in the batter and bake for about 1–1¼ hours until risen, golden brown and firm.
4. Remove from the oven and cool in the tin for 20 minutes, then turn out on to a serving plate. Remove the disc of parchment and dust with icing sugar. Serve cut in wedges.

Points per serving: 3½
Total Points per recipe: 20½

Carrot, Date and Oaty Squares

Makes: 12 portions

Preparation time: 20 minutes
+ 35–40 minutes baking
Calories per portion: 175

Freezing: recommended

Tray bakes are not only easy to make, they are oh-so-simple to serve!

2 carrots, grated coarsely
100 g (3½ oz) stoned dates, chopped
1 tablespoon lemon juice
1 tablespoon clear honey
low-fat cooking spray
175 g (6 oz) wholemeal flour
175 g (6 oz) porridge oats
75 g (2¾ oz) low-fat spread
50 g (1¾ oz) soft brown sugar

1. Put the carrots, dates, lemon juice and honey into a small pan with 2 tablespoons of water. Bring to the boil, stirring, then lower to simmer and cook for about 10 minutes until soft and pulpy. Leave to cool.
2. Line the base of an 18 cm (7-inch) square shallow cake tin with non-stick baking parchment and lightly spray the sides with low-fat cooking spray.
3. Preheat the oven to Gas Mark 4/180°C/350°F. Mix the flour and oats together, then rub in the low-fat spread. Mix in the sugar. Sprinkle half of this mixture on the cake tin base, pressing down lightly with the back of a spoon. Spoon the carrot and date mixture over and cover with the rest of the oat mixture. Press this down lightly too.
4. Bake for about 35–40 minutes until golden brown and cooked through. Remove and cool it until just warm, then cut it into 12 squares in the tin. Turn them out of the tin and cool them completely. Store in an air-tight container.

Points per portion: 2½
Total Points per recipe: 31½

Coffee Meringue Kisses

Makes: 12 single meringues or 6 cream meringues

Preparation time: 15 minutes
+ 1¼–1½ hours baking
Calories per meringue: 35;
2 meringues with cream 125

Freezing: recommended

2 free-range egg whites
a pinch of salt or a dribble of
    lemon juice
100 g (3½ oz) caster sugar
1 tablespoon coffee granules
100 ml (3 fl oz) whipping
    cream (optional)

A little light indulgence –
drop spoonfuls of thick glossy
coffee meringue on to baking
sheets and cook them until
crisp on the outside and gooey
in the centre. Eat them as
they are, or if you really want
to go all the way, then
sandwich them with a thin
layer of whipped cream,
allowing 1 teaspoon for 2
meringues.

1. Use an electric whisk unless you are used to beating long and
hard. Make sure the bowl is spotlessly clean and free of any grease
– it is best to scald it with some boiling water and a drop of
washing-up liquid.
2. Preheat the oven to Gas Mark 1/140°C/275°F. Line a flat baking
sheet with non-stick baking paper.
3. Whisk the egg whites with the salt or lemon juice until they
form softly firm peaks – that is, they flop over a little when lifted
up. The foam peak should waggle when shaken. The egg whites
should not be dry and grainy or the sugar will not incorporate well.
4. Now whisk in the sugar, a spoonful at a time, until you have a
thick, glossy foam. Finally, whisk in the coffee granules.
5. Drop 12 spoonfuls of mixture on the prepared sheet. It doesn't
matter if they are an irregular shape. That makes them look more
inviting.
6. Bake for 1¼ to 1½ hours until the outside is crisp and you can
lift the meringues off the sheets. Cool them on a wire rack.
7. If you wish to make cream meringues, beat the cream until it
forms soft peaks and sandwich between two meringues. Eat quickly.

Points per meringue: ½; 2 meringues with cream 1
Total Points per recipe: 5½; with cream 17

Honey Roasted Fruit

Serves: 4

Preparation time: 10 minutes
+ 15 minutes cooking
Calories per serving: with
banana 85; with pineapple 85;
with rhubarb 30

Freezing: not recommended

500 g (1 lb 2 oz) fresh rhubarb
    or pineapple rings, or 2 large
    bananas
1 tablespoon clear honey
1 teaspoon low-fat spread
juice of 1 small orange

Instead of stewing fruit, cook
it quickly in a pan over fairly
high heat. It tastes delicious
and doesn't swim around in
juices. This is ideal for rhubarb,
fresh pineapple or bananas.
Serve the fruit chilled with
low-fat plain or fruit yogurt,
adding Points as necessary.

1. Cut the fruit into bite-size chunks. For washed rhubarb or juicy
pineapple, pat dry with kitchen paper.
2. Heat the honey, low-fat spread and orange juice in a wide
shallow pan. When it is bubbling, add the fruit of your choice.
3. Cook over a fairly high heat, shaking the pan occasionally and
stirring carefully so as not to break up the fruit. Pineapple and
bananas will take about 5 minutes, rhubarb about 10. You will have
to gauge the temperature and time so that it cooks by the time the
liquid has reduced to a syrup.
4. Cool in the pan for 10 minutes, then transfer the fruit to 4 serving
dishes. Allow them to cool to room temperature before serving.

Points per serving: with bananas 1½; with rhubarb ½;
with pineapple 1½
Total Points per recipe: with bananas 6½; with rhubarb 2½;
with pineapple 6

Kiwi and Melon Salad with Sweet Lime Sprinkle

Serves: 4

Preparation time: 15 minutes
+ 15 minutes marinating
Calories per serving: with
sugar 70; with sweetener 60

Freezing: not recommended

A simple fruit salad using just
two main fruits with a third
as a juice. As this is not
cooked, you can use artificial
sweetener instead of sugar if
you prefer.

4 ripe kiwi fruits
1 small melon, e.g. Charentais,
 Ogen or Galia
grated zest and juice of 1 lime
1 tablespoon caster sugar or
 1 teaspoon granulated
 sweetener
1 tablespoon chopped fresh
 mint (optional)

1. Using the tip of a small sharp knife, carefully cut out the hard
core at the top of the kiwi fruits, then peel thinly and cut each
kiwi into wedges. Place in a bowl.
2. Halve the melon, scoop out the seeds, then peel and cut into
chunks. Add to the kiwi.
3. Sprinkle the lime juice over and leave to marinate for 15 minutes
or so in the fridge.
4. Just before serving, mix the grated lime zest with the sugar
or sweetener and sprinkle it over the fruits, along with the mint
(if using). Serve fairly soon after.

Points per serving: with sugar 2; with sweetener 1½
Total Points per recipe: with sugar 7½; with sweetener 6

Prune Tea Loaf

Makes: 12 slices

Preparation time: 10 minutes
+ 1¼–1½ hours baking
Calories per slice: 120

Freezing: recommended

This has a texture like a
sticky, moist malt loaf. It uses
a prune purée instead of fat,
but does take a little longer
than normal tea loaves to
bake. Ideally, wrap it in
clingfilm and store it for at
least a day before cutting so it
becomes slightly sticky.

400 g (14 oz) canned prunes
 in fruit juice
100 g (3½ oz) All-Bran
 breakfast cereal
200 ml (7 fl oz) skimmed milk
low-fat cooking spray
100 g (3½ oz) self-raising flour
1 teaspoon mixed spice
1 free-range egg
50 g (1¾ oz) soft brown sugar
75 g (2¾ oz) sultanas

1. Drain the prunes but reserve the juice. Remove the stones from
the prunes and discard (they are easy to pull out), then mash them
to a pulp with a fork.
2. Mix the All-Bran in a bowl with the prune juice, prune pulp and
milk. Set aside for about 2 hours until completely softened.
3. Meanwhile, spray a 900 g (2 lb) loaf tin with low-fat cooking spray
and line the base with non-stick baking parchment. When the
All-Bran has soaked, preheat the oven to Gas Mark 4/180°C/350°F.
4. Sift the flour with the spice and beat into the mixture along
with the egg, sugar and sultanas.
5. Spoon the mixture into the prepared tin and bake for 1¼ – 1½
hours until firm when pressed on the top. Cool in the tin for 30
minutes before turning out of the tin to cool completely. When
cold, wrap in clingfilm and store for at least a day before cutting
into thin slices.

Points per slice: 1½
Total Points per recipe: 20

Cocoa Sponge Fingers with Raspberry Crush

Serves: 6

Preparation time: 20 minutes
+ 7 minutes baking
Calories per serving: without
honey 170; with honey 175

Freezing: recommended

2 free-range eggs
90 g (3¼ oz) caster sugar
90 g (3¼ oz) plain flour
15 g (½ oz) cocoa powder
200 g (7 oz) carton very-low-fat
    plain fromage frais
1 tablespoon clear honey or
    artificial sweetener, to taste
250 g (9 oz) ripe raspberries

Chocolate cake may be a
favourite dessert for many of
us, but it is often high in fat
and Calories. This recipe uses
lower fat cocoa powder but
tastes just as rich. Delicious
served with very-low-fat plain
fromage frais sweetened with
some crushed raspberries.

1. First, make the sponge fingers. Preheat the oven to Gas Mark 6/
200°C/400°F. Line a baking sheet with non-stick baking parchment.
2. Place the eggs and sugar in a large heatproof bowl over a pan of
simmering water. Using an electric, rotary or balloon whisk, beat
them steadily until you have a firm thick foam. It is ready when
the pale, thick, golden foam holds its shape when folded back
on itself.
3. Remove from the heat and continue whisking for another 5
minutes until the mixture is cool. Sift the flour and cocoa powder
and carefully fold them into the foam, using a large metal spoon.
4. Spoon into a piping bag fitted with a large plain nozzle and pipe
thick fingers about 10 cm (4 inches) or more in length.
5. Bake for 5–7 minutes until the outside is crisp and the texture
feels firm when lightly pressed. Cool slightly, then remove the
sponge fingers to a wire tray with a palette knife.
6. For the raspberry cream, sweeten the fromage frais with honey
or sweetener. Crush some of the riper berries and mix these in,
then fold in the rest. Divide between six sundae dishes, allowing
two sponge fingers each. The remainder can be frozen or nibbled
later on.

Points per serving: 3
Total Points per recipe: without honey 16; with honey 17½

Banana Yogurt Sundae

Serves: 4

Preparation time: 10 minutes
+ chilling
Calories per serving: 170

Freezing: not recommended

2 large or 4 small ripe bananas
4 teaspoons dark muscovado or
    soft brown sugar
2 pinches of freshly grated
    nutmeg or cinnamon or
    mixed spice
300 g (10 oz) low-fat Bio-yogurt
2 reduced-fat digestive biscuits

Ripe bananas are sweeter and
more creamy than pale yellow
or green ones. Eat them when
they have bright yellow skins
with little black spots. This is
a quick and easy pud, ideal for
mid-week eating. Bio-yogurt
has a mild flavour, so it is ideal
for desserts. Use reduced-fat
digestive biscuits for a crunchy
topping.

1. Peel and slice the bananas into four sundae dishes or wine glasses.
2. Mix the sugar and spice gently into the yogurt. It doesn't matter
if it is a little streaky – that looks attractive.
3. Spoon the mixture on top of the fruit. Crush the biscuits with
your fingers and add them on top of the yogurt. Serve lightly chilled.

Points per serving: 3
Total Points per recipe: 11

Low-Fat Sticky Gingerbread

Makes: about 20 slices

Preparation time: 15 minutes
+ cooling + 1¼–1½ hours
cooking
Calories per serving: 100

Freezing: recommended

Easy to make – you just mix a batter with dry ingredients, then bake. There's no need for extra butter or low-fat spread because it's beautifully moist.

40 g (1½ oz) low-fat spread
2 tablespoons marmalade
100 g (3½ fl oz) golden syrup
100 g (3½ fl oz) black treacle
50 g (1¾ oz) soft brown sugar
150 ml (¼ pint) skimmed milk
low-fat cooking spray
75 g (2¾ oz) wholemeal flour
75 g (2¾ oz) self-raising flour
1 teaspoon ground ginger
1 teaspoon mixed spice
¼ teaspoon bicarbonate of soda
50 g (1¾ oz) porridge oats
1 free-range egg

1. Put the low-fat spread, marmalade, syrup, treacle and sugar into a large saucepan and heat until bubbling, stirring well. Simmer gently for a few minutes until the sugar has melted and the mixture is no longer gritty. Remove and cool, then mix in the milk.
2. Meanwhile, spray an 18 cm (7 inch) square, deep cake tin with low-fat cooking spray and line the base and sides with non-stick baking parchment, cutting it to fit.
3. Preheat the oven to Gas Mark 2/150°C/275°F. Mix the flours well with the spices, bicarbonate and oats.
4. When the mixture in the pan is cold, beat in the dry ingredients and the egg until you have a smooth mixture. Pour into the prepared tin.
5. Bake for 1¼ to 1½ hours until the cake is risen and firm when pressed on top. Cool in the tin for ½ hour, then turn out and cool completely. Peel off the paper, wrap the cake in clingfilm and leave for a day or more to become nice and sticky. The gingerbread will keep for about a week.

Points per serving: 1½
Total Points per recipe: 30½

Pancakes with Strawberries and Ice Cream

Serves: 4

Preparation time: 15 minutes
+ ½ hour softening (optional)
+ 15 minutes cooking
Calories per serving: with
icing sugar 235; without icing
sugar 225

Freezing: recommended

Pancakes can be quite low in Calories and Points, especially if you cook them in a good non-stick pan and use low-fat cooking spray. The secret of wafer-thin pancakes is to get the pan hot first of all.

125 g (4½ oz) plain flour, sifted
    with a pinch of salt
1 free-range egg
½ teaspoon vanilla essence
300 ml (½ pint) skimmed milk
low-fat cooking spray
250 g (9 oz) strawberries
1 tablespoon fresh lemon juice
1–2 teaspoons icing sugar or
    artificial sweetener
4 scoops low-fat ice cream

1. Put the flour, egg, vanilla and milk into a food processor and whizz to a batter. Alternatively, put the flour in a bowl, break in the egg, add the vanilla and milk and gradually beat to a batter. (If you like, you can leave this for ½ hour but modern flours don't need much softening.)
2. Pour the batter into a jug. Heat a small non-stick frying-pan. When you can feel a good heat rising, spray it lightly with low-fat cooking spray. Pour in about 3 tablespoons of batter and quickly swirl the pan to coat the base.
3. Cook until the batter becomes firm and tiny bubbles appear. Using a palette knife, flip the pancake over to cook the other side briefly. Remove to a wire rack and cover with a clean tea towel.
4. Repeat with the remaining batter. You should get about 12 pancakes – certainly at least 8 – from this recipe. Freeze any that are left over.
5. Meanwhile, crush half the strawberries with the lemon juice and icing sugar or sweetener and slice the remainder. Mix together. Divide the mixture between the pancakes and roll them up.
6. Place 2 pancakes on each of 4 plates and top them with a scoop of ice cream. Eat quickly.

Points per serving: 3½
Total Points per recipe: with icing sugar 14½; without icing sugar 13½

Index